Things That Go SQUEAK in the Night

Also by Gregory Clark in Totem Books

THE BIRD OF PROMISE

OUTDOORS WITH GREGORY CLARK

FISHING WITH GREGORY CLARK

GRANDMA PREFERRED STEAK

Things That Go SQUEAK in the Night

and other stories

by Gregory Clark

A TOTEM BOOK
TORONTO

Things That Go Squeak in the Night
by Gregory Clark

First published 1976 by
Optimum Publishing Company Limited
Montreal, Quebec
This edition published 1978
by TOTEM BOOKS
a division of
Collins Publishers
100 Lesmill Road, Don Mills, Ontario

Canadian Cataloguing in Publication Data

Clark, Gregory, 1892-1977.
Things that go squeak in the night and other stories

Selections from the newspaper column "The packsack."

ISBN 0-00-216689-5 pa.

I. Title.

PS8505.L32T55 1978 C818.5'2'08 C78-001245-3
PR9199.3.C52T55 1978

Design—Max Newton

Printed in Canada by
Universal Printers Ltd. Winnipeg

Foreword

This new collection is from a large body of Gregory Clark's work identified in daily newspapers as "The Packsack."

The first book in this series, *Outdoors with Gregory Clark*, published in 1971, is made up entirely of stories and observations drawn from Greg Clark's six decades of experience as a devoted and accomplished outdoorsman and naturalist.

The second volume, *Grandma Preferred Steak*, (1974) is an assortment of stories about people, wild and otherwise, who dwell outside the territory occupied by all the feathered, furred and web-footed personae of the first book.

This new book is wide-ranging, a random walk with Greg Clark in all the regions he has lived and fished and summered in—and decorated with laughter—as newspaperman and traveller. Here are friends and strangers, people you may meet once a day or once in a lifetime, disclosed.

Hugh Shaw

Gregory Clark

Contents

Things That Go Squeak in the Night

Furtive, cautious sounds are far more irritating than good loud forthright sounds. My neighbor is a gentle and thoughtful man. But he is also an early riser. And when there is a light snowfall, he is up with the lark or the starlings to shovel it off.

Fearing to disturb the neighborhood, he shovels very soft. Very soft, very lightly he scrapes and scratches and scoops with his tin shovel. He does not work fast. He works slowly. He takes long pauses while he surveys the early morn and doubtless casts a few kindly, apologetic glances up at the curtained windows of his neighbors.

Up in those rooms, his poor neighbors, sunk deep in that lovely last desperate hour of slumber, battle against consciousness as these soft, furtive sounds of shovelling tap, tap, tap at the door of consciousness. They wake. They lie listening, to identify the faint curious scraping. They jump hotly out of bed to peer past the blinds, to see what mischief is going on. It is only our gentle and thoughtful neighbor, delicately removing his snow.

It would be better, far, if he were a surly and heartless man, who attacked his snow noisily, furiously and with speed. It would be sooner over, and we could dive back into that last lovely sleep before the clock buzzes.

If a neighbor has to take his car out of the garage at 3 a.m., we like him to take it out with a good bang, and back her out with decision. At least we know what is going on. But to hear the creepy, furtive sounds of a thoughtful neighbor trying to do the same job without

continued

disturbing the neighborhood, is not merely to disturb the whole neighborhood, but to leave us all wondering anxiously what is amiss with the poor devil.

After Many a Long Sweet Summer

Summer cottage resorts are inhabited mostly by families who have been going to the same cottage for years, even for two or three generations. Flibbertygibbets, of course, go to summer hotels, and wander from place to place over the years. And there are cottage resorts that consist of the type of house which is not quite fit for sentimental attachment, and is therefore rented to transient families that come and go, seldom returning.

But to those families who belong in the first category, those who year after year, and generation upon generation, return to the same dear spot regardless of peace or war, hard times or affluent, their summer cottage becomes a more beloved premises than any other home they live in, or have lived in. I know that in the war, when I was scared stiff and felt my final hour had come, it was the summer home with which I had been familiar since childhood that swam into my vision as I tried to hang onto some intimate recollection in whose company I might happily be bumped off. I mentioned this to a good many comrades, and those who belonged in the category agreed that they had the same experience.

It is therefore a sad thing that it is at the summer cottage that a man first becomes conscious of the decline of his vigor. For forty or fifty long sweet summers he has been jumping into the skiff from the dock in a certain, natural, easy fashion. All of a sudden the day comes when he jumps in the accustomed way, and darn near breaks his neck.

For nigh on half a century, you have been hauling the rowboat up on the dock to empty the rainwater out of it. You grab the skiff by the nose, give it an easy hoist to set the nose on the dock's edge, then laying back your weight, you haul. And ups-a-daisy she slides.

Then there arrives the day when you give it a hoist, and it comes only half way. In astonishment, you give it a bigger hoist, and something goes snick in your spinal column. You call your daughter to come and help you haul the skiff onto the wharf.

Paddles don't turn the same way they did; cookie tins, instead of going slick back up onto the kitchen shelf, miss by a foot and come clattering down for all to hear.

In cities, you can get through the routine of the day without finding out what another year has done to you. But at the summer cottage, alas, that sweet beloved abode, everything around the place goes yah, yah, yah, at you.

Airedale Eyes

Certain human beings have what might be described as Airedale eyes. An Airedale terrier has a characteristic

continued

shrewd, cold, appraising eye. People fortunate enough to possess the Airedale eye are vested with an air of command without having uttered a single word.

Some years ago, a small item appeared in a newspaper suggesting that if the reader found, through shyness or habit, that he had difficulty in meeting and holding the eye of another person during conversation, a simple trick is to look, not at the eye of the other person, but at the bridge of the nose between the eyes.

On reading this, I immediately sought out a couple of characters who had Airedale eyes and with whom I experienced that very difficulty; they dominated me with their hard, bold stare. To my astonishment and delight, I discovered that by following instructions and centering my gaze on the bridges of their noses between their eyes, not only was all their dominating power lost, but they seemed somehow frustrated and flustered. It would almost appear that I had developed Airedale eyes.

Excited by this discovery, I went forth hunting for victims of the new technique. Policemen, box office men at theatres and hockey arenas, bank managers and plumbers. The trick worked like magic.

In employing this technique, you will at first find that your eyes are a little inclined to slide away from the bridge of the opponent's nose and seek either one or other of his eyes. But after some practice, it becomes second nature to focus on the nose bridge and hold it there, while coolly conversing, for as long as necessary.

It is not necessary to withhold your gaze from your adversary's eyes throughout a conversation. After a few moments, having either escaped the domination of the other's, or established the domination of your own, your eyes meet quite pleasantly. During the war, I found the British War Office, Admiralty and Air Force Headquarters and similar high places filled with gentlemen with an Airedale eye. My job was vastly simplified by this nose bridge trick. The gentlemen in question mostly had very fine nose bridges on which to focus.

From all this you will further gather that a shy little guy will go through an awful hocus-pocus to set himself at ease in the presence of those happy, happy mortals who are not shy.

Distress Signals

Many of us enjoy friendship more than we do our own health.

A cousin of mine can eat neither chicken nor veal without the most violent reactions. But I have seen him manfully sit through a dinner and make a great to-do about enjoying the feast though what he is eating is literally poison. Onions are poison to others, but I have seen alliophobes, as we call onion-haters, rather than distress a hostess, serenely downing soup or salad that, within an hour or two, would have them in agony.

But it is hard to say whether the martyrs are a greater nuisance than the hypochondriacs who, wholly inconsiderate of anybody's feelings, protect their own in loud and emphatic declarations of what they will or will not eat. At a dinner party lately, a middle-aged lady caused considerable embarrassment by rejecting certain foods, giving at the same time emphatic descriptions of the effects of these foods on her interior economy, much to her own and nobody else's entertainment. After dinner, out on the back lawn, I kept company with a poor kindly

continued

man who, despite his allergies, had quietly poisoned himself rather than join company with the self-protective lady. I slipped in the kitchen and got him a dose of baking soda.

It was my duty to drive the two of them home around midnight. They sat in the back seat, side by side, the one repeating her anatomical objections to the dinner, the other just repeating.

And I don't know which of them gave me the greater pain.

Compact

We pint sized men are secretly very pleased to hear these small motor cars being called compact cars.

It is very pleasant to feel oneself compact instead of peewee. On our drivers' licenses, hunting licenses, and insurance identity cards, it is going to be nice from now on to put "compact" in the space formerly reserved for 5 foot 3 or thereabouts. We assume that from now on, novelists and writers of romance will refer to us not as small men but as compact men, even if we have to play the villain's role, which so often falls to our lot. Maybe not the chief villain, who is usually described as heavily-built, but his associates, the minor villains.

As a matter of fact, compact is a word that should have come into popular usage long ago to describe us handy-sized little whiffets. The dictionary says compact means "joined or packed together; closely and firmly united;

dense, solid." If you look at us closely, you will see that this is so. We have all the same limbs, parts and organs as larger specimens of our kind, but they are not so loosely thrown together. We're snug. There is no waste space about us, as there usually is in large men. Why a man has to jack himself up on four foot legs has always been a mystery to us compact types. We fit into life so much more easily.

It is going to be fun for us to watch the uncompact majority of mankind trying to be comfortable in these new, modern and eminently sensible compact cars.

Strained

My wife and I decided for a lark to revisit a tea room where years ago, we had done much of our courting. We will call it Ye Olde Dumpe Tea Room, and is located upstairs over some shops.

We even had the good fortune to find one or two of the old waitresses who remembered us. I ordered tea and cinnamon toast. My wife asked for a pot of cocoa and wafers. It was amusing to be sitting in the old familiar corner.

When my wife poured the cocoa, something went plop out of the spout. She took a spoon and examined the plop. It separated into three very drowned cockroaches. Reluctantly, we called our old friend, the waitress. She was horror-stricken.

"Oh, Mrs. Clark," she gasped, "I can't see how this

continued

could possibly have happened. We strain everything in the kitchen."

This business of straining everything in the kitchen is not confined, unfortunately, to Ye Olde Dumpe Tea Room. When I was a young newspaperman, I had never heard of a public relations man. If I wanted to see a big business man, I went and saw him. If he wouldn't see me, I went and interviewed his rival. That fixed him.

The same in politics. Even the biggest men in public life did not feel it necessary to hedge themselves in behind public relations experts. Perhaps, in those old days, there weren't so many cockroaches to get in the cocoa. Things did not have to be strained.

Today, everything is strained. All governments and government departments, all great institutions as well as private businesses are safeguarded by large staffs of cockroach strainers. And I am not horrified but actually filled with a mischievous delight when out of the spout of big business and big affairs something goes plop.

Gun Play

What utterly astonishes me in the TV westerns is the way everybody can shoot with a six-shooter. Not only the marshals and famous outlaws can whip their weapons from their hips with lightning speed but they always kill their man. Dead as a tick. And even no-account cow hands have the same gift.

In real life, as I experienced it in the first or Mud war,

and in the more recent war, hardly anybody could hit a barn door with a pistol. Pistol shooting is an art as far removed or advanced from rifle shooting as croquet is from tiddleywinks. For three and a half years of my life in that first war I carried, day and night, a trusty forty-five strapped to my midriff. And I don't recall ever having hit anything with it. I shot it any number of times, and scared the stuffing out of my immediate neighbors, some rats and, on occasion, myself. We carried pistols for reasons of morale. On rare occasions, they proved useful, but they were "belly guns." When serviceable, they were fired at point-blank range. And even then, the target was usually winged, not killed.

To see these western bad men and good men, legs astraddle like a little boy who has had an accident in his pants, snatching forth their guns to fire without aim, invariably getting the enemy through the heart makes those of us, to the number of a hundred thousand or so still living, who carried pistols in war feel very inferior, or else derisive.

Meeting

It is hard to say which is more disturbing; old eyes in a young face, or young eyes in an old face. I was obliged to call at a shabby little house in a derelict section of town, and there I saw a small boy of no more than six or seven out of whose head stared the eyes of a shrewd old man. There was no shyness in them, no fear. There was just a

continued

sort of derision. Indeed, come to think of it, there was a kind of courage.

He needed it. The dire heat of summer was on us all, all around him was dirt and poverty and the hopelessness of parents and elders who could think of nothing but their misfortunes. And while I stood at the door talking of these misfortunes to the elders, the little boy stood back, silent, languid, and penetrating me with his strange old eyes.

Then up the street came this old man, in black, walking heavily with the heat. And he turned in the walk and joined us at the door. His type is not unfamiliar in these derelict regions of the town. He wears his collar back to front. Often, they are old men. They puff.

When he looked at me, I was as disturbed by his gaze as I was by that of the little boy. For out of his aged and wrinkled face stared the eyes of a child. No trace of weariness showed in their blue depth. They were full of shyness, enquiry and even of fear. They were the beautiful, gentle, trusting eyes of a child.

He did not stand at the door, as I was doing. He pushed straight into the dirty little house. He sat down. He looked at the boy and nothing else.

It was a weird thing to see those two sets of eyes meeting; the old eyes in the child's face, the child's eyes in the clergyman's face.

"I have come to tell you," the clergyman said, "I have found a place for you at a summer camp. I have an old fishing rod I can lend you, with a line, and sinkers and hooks. I will teach you how to catch grasshoppers for the best bait. . . . "

That is where I left.

How Trouble Starts

Presidents and general managers sometimes come down off their lofty perches with disastrous results to the business. Quite by accident, the president of a thriving industry overheard a long distance telephone call being carried on by a quite minor member of the sales management staff of the firm. The president had observed a particularly beautiful girl in the elevator that morning, and had decided to take a walk through the office to have another look at her. Even presidents are capable of such interests. While on tour, he had paused by this young man's desk, and heard the conversation. When it was concluded, the president said:

"Now, couldn't that matter have been handled by a letter and a postage stamp? How much did that phone call cost?"

It had cost $3.75.

So the president got launched on one of those housecleaning rampages that happen even in thriving businesses. Not having discovered the pretty girl, he stamped back into his lofty office and demanded immediately to be shown the figures for long distance telephone calls for the past month for all departments. He was shocked. He sent for the figures for the year, and called an urgent conference of the entire management, at which he fumed and raged about the reckless overhead not only in telephone tolls but in several other things which a president, in one of his tantrums, can think up: expense accounts, mileage rates paid for the use of salesmen's cars, the cost of building maintenance, the number of cleaning women employed.

The result was an economy wave. Everybody in the

continued

whole organization got mad. Nobody took a chance. Nothing but letters were written. No long distance calls, no wires. Paper work began to pile up. Three of the best stenographers went and got married in sheer disgust. The assistant sales manager went to a competitor. Five cleaning women were laid off. A sour spirit grew and grew. It will be a wonder if the present year will show the volume of last year. And nobody, not even the president, knows that it all started with him seeing a pretty girl in the elevator.

Who's That?

I will now tell you how you will know when you are getting old. It is when you are looking through an old snapshot album that nobody has looked at for thirty years and you see a snapshot of yourself with five other guys. And you have forgotten who two of them are.

There you are, the six of you, laughing at the camera. Maybe you are holding up a string of fish among the lot of you. How lean and gawky you look, yourself! Did I ever look like that, you say to yourself. And your family merely hoots.

"That's Bob Jenkins," you say, pointing, "and that's Cec Perry, and there's what's-his-name Hall. But who is that, now?"

And across the years, two faces smile at you, utter strangers. Yet for a day or a year at least they were your companions.

As you turn the pages of the album, there you are with

your arm around a girl's shoulder and she has her arm around your waist. A brown-haired girl, a Mona Lisa smile.

"And who's that!" cries your wife and all your granddaughters.

"I think," you say, "I think her name was Elva. Or was it Flo?"

But there, among the derisive cries of your women, old and young, you do not remember her name at all.

Who Wants a Perfect Day?

A young woman of my family has just returned from a year and more in art colleges in Britain, and travelling student-style in France, Italy, Austria. And her very first question, on returning home to Canada was:

"Where's the sky?"

It is now her impression that we have no sky in Canada.

"In England, in London especially," she says, "you look at the sky every day, and many times a day. And it is not for the reason you jump at. It is not because of your interest in England's weather. It is because the sky is there, part of the view, part of life itself. It is close, intimate, as real as the earth or the buildings or the landscape. It is included with everything else."

I asked if the sky in Europe were bluer than we have

continued

it here in Canada. She thought not. Was it moving, with clouds? Possibly.

But this absence of sky in Canada disturbed her, and for a week after her return, she watched us, and other people.

"Canadians never look at the sky," she declared. "They don't even look at the stars."

And she described how tender the stars are in England, how radiant in Italy, how effulgent in Austria.

"In London," she said, "you will commonly see people looking at the sky at night, attentively, appreciatively."

"Maybe," I suggested, "it's the effect of all those pubs . . ."

But now that I recall my various years in Europe, in the wars and on travels, I have the impression which many an old soldier will confirm out of his own memory, that there is a sky over England, Scotland, France and Italy which does seem to come down closer to earth than our Canadian sky.

A most interesting national poll of Canadians might be taken along these lines:

What sort of sky do you prefer?

Do you prefer an all blue sky?

Do you prefer a blue sky with moving clouds?

Do you prefer a cloudy sky?

Do you prefer a grey sky with rain?

From listening to Canadians for the past two generations or so, it is my impression that an overwhelming proportion of Canadians want nothing but blue sky. Their idea of a perfect day is blue sky, bright sun, from daybreak to sunset. If there is no wind at all, so much the better, but a little cooling breeze might come into their picture of the ideal day, depending on the temperature.

It is on such a day that everybody exclaims: "What a perfect day!" Since in most parts of Canada we get any number of such days, anywhere from fifty to a hundred and fifty of them a year, it is not as if we had few of them, as people do in Britain and other countries where there is a heavy preponderance of cloudy and wet days. In England and Scotland, people in general have a real love for cloudy days, even grey and wet days. Especially in the country, you will see people out walking and moving about their business with every evidence of enjoyment of the weather, regardless of what it is. Canadians resent such weather and show it in every way possible. Impatiently, they await the blue sky.

Personally, I have never been so soddenly bored as by the interminable blue days of the Bahamas or the tropical countries I have been briefly marooned in.

The Quarter

The wayside restaurant at which we had lunch is all window in front, a sort of super picture window. You park your car on the gravel in front, the nose of your car a few feet from the window. Even with nothing but a bunch of parked cars' noses to look at, it is pleasant to have lunch at the tables by this spacious window.

The bill was small. The tip for the little waitress who had served us with extra amiable attention was in change. Quarters, three of them. When my wife and I went out and got in our car, we were just in time to see two ladies take their place at the table we had just vacated.

Our dishes were still on the table, and the lady who took my chair, a woman in her thirties, stylishly dressed in summer white, a cool-faced, competent-looking person,

continued

pushed the dishes away from in front of her and beheld my coins that had been secreted under the tea saucer.

To my astonishment, I saw her flick the coins with her finger tip. I told my wife to look. The handsome, practical-looking lady calmly placed her pucker-string white purse on the table, opened it, picked up a quarter, placed it in her purse, drew the pucker string, shoved the remaining two quarters back under the saucer, and then glanced up to look straight into our shocked stare, not ten feet from her.

She was unruffled. She did not even flush. But she refused to raise her eyes again, though we sat there a long moment while I resurrected certain profanities I had not uttered since the battle of Passchendaele.

The two, both far better clothed than most people, sat in calm conversation, and studied the menu.

"Fantastic!" said my wife.

I got out and returned into the restaurant.

I took another quarter from my pocket and went over to the table. I shoved the saucer aside, and made certain only two coins remained.

"Don't touch this one," I said, politely, as I laid the second quarter alongside the others.

She never batted an eye.

Some people have massive self-control.

Fate of a Bold Bullfrog

Edmond King, a farmer friend of mine who works one of the less arable regions of the Georgian Bay, encountered a very large bullfrog on the marshy beach of his property. He used to see it regularly in his passage along the path, and he grew impressed with the pomp and dignity of the creature as the bullfrog grew more and more accustomed to Edmond's presence.

Edmond took a long stem of timothy with the seed head on it and squatting down, reached out and tickled the bullfrog's nose. The bullfrog stonily submitted to the indignity. Edmond drew the timothy head across one eye of the frog. Some seeds got in the eye, and the bullfrog indignantly, and with almost human impatience, wiped the seed from his eye. Edmond ran back three or four paces, in pretended fear. The bullfrog was suitably impressed.

Next day, Edmond repeated the tickling with the timothy, and this time, the bullfrog opened his capacious mouth and snapped in the timothy head. Edmond gave a sharp jerk, and the seed-loaded timothy stayed in the frog's mouth. With his forepaws, one after the other, in literally fat-man fury, the bullfrog fought to remove the dry and unpleasant timothy head from his mouth. And when he had got it cleared, he again glared at Edmond, reared up threateningly, and again, Edmond, in mock terror, ran back several paces.

The next morning, Edmond approached with the timothy straw and the bullfrog, after sagacious consideration, reared up. Edmond ran. The bullfrog took three leaps after him, and Edmond ran farther up the hill. The bullfrog returned to his usual sitting place and resumed

continued

his cogitations with a most self-satisfied and even more imposing stance.

The following morning, Edmond approached with due caution and respect. The bullfrog reared up on sight of him and glared menacingly.

Edmond took a timid step backwards. Instantly, the bullfrog launched himself, and took four or five great leaps. Edmond retreated with equal jumps. The bullfrog, satisfied it had inspired terror in the man, stood his ground a long moment and then retreated to his stand. For several days, Edmond succeeded in inviting this preposterous performance. As a philosopher, he was delighted to know that valor can be induced, and that the lowliest of creatures is capable of the feelings of superiority more familiar in man. Then, a lady cottager, who hates reptiles and batrachians, killed the poor bullfrog with a stick.

The Whiskers Wilters

A commonplace question among men is: "What razor blades do you use?" The inference may be drawn that men are vaguely dissatisfied with their blades. The average man obviously does quite a bit of shopping around in blades, trying this one and that one, as is evident in the variety of blades for sale and the lively advertising of them.

Today a man puts everything up to the blade. He slaps on a little new-fangled cream of some sort, brushless or to be brushed, and then immediately goes to work with the blade, expecting the worst. If he would only remember his father, or his father's father, and the great days of the barbering trade when half the men in the world, if not more, never dreamed of shaving themselves but went to the barber shop each day, the modern shaver would understand what a good shave consisted of.

It consisted, first of all, of reclining back in a great chair far more comfortable and flexible than a dentist's chair. Next, after a few cheery words from the barber, a hot wet towel was wrapped around the chin, neck and cheeks, with a tiny peep-hole left for the patient's nose, so he could breathe.

Hot and stinging, the moist towel clung to the face, wilting every whisker. You could feel the stubble melting. Off whisked the towel, and another, hotter, moister than the first was deftly slapped around chin, neck and cheeks again. Tingling, you listened, for your eyes were also covered by the towel, to the barber preparing the lather mug. You could hear him walk over to the tap, run it generously, to get the water really hot.

Off came the towel; and there stood the barber, mug and brush in hand, whipping up a good, rich lather with a boiling hot brush. This he lathered richly all over your chin, neck, cheeks, finally rubbing it into your stubble with fingertips. Surely no whisker could resist a blade now.

But no. This was not the end. On came the third hot, steaming towel for a brief moment. It was whipped off, and a second and final lather was given with the brush.

Then, and only then, using a five dollar razor with a blade honed and stropped to surgical perfection, did the barber presume to attack your whiskers. It was ten parts lather, one part blade. What the modern razor blade is expected to be is a wire cutter.

Predicament

The season for fish stories being again upon us, it is as well to have a couple of new ones handy for any occasion that may arise.

For example, Wilfred Churchman of Saskatchewan gave us this one to remind us, he said, that his province, despite its prairie identity, is three fifths covered by as beautiful forest, lakes, rock, and wilderness as is to be found anywhere in Canada.

One of these lakes, pretty far north, is Churchman's favorite. It is about forty feet deep. The fish in it come in layers. The first layer are perch, running up to two or three pounds, and about ten feet of the upper area of the depth are solid perch. Next comes a solid layer of jackfish or pike, running up to twenty-five, twenty-eight pounds, or thereabouts. But down in the lower layer are Churchman's favorites, the lake trout, running up to, oh, forty, fifty pounds. So far he has been completely baffled in his efforts to get at the trout, because if he fishes with bait, the perch tear it to flinders before it can sink ten feet. If he uses artificial lures, the savage jackfish or pike rip the lure to bits before it can sink through that layer down to the trout.

He figured out a system. He brought twenty-five feet of stove pipe up, not without considerable trouble and expense to that remote lake. He lowered the pipe down through the two layers of perch and jackfish, and then dropped his trout lure through to the trout. They took, all right. But they were too big for him to haul back up the stove pipe.

He is now negotiating with the bush pilots and dog team drivers to bring him in thirty feet of culvert. And all Churchman's friends are eagerly awaiting results.

Thought for April

When we think of the word power, we usually first think of electric current, engines, jet aircraft or some such marvel of the age. In our minds power has also something to do with big nations.

But there is another power that we can make ourselves aware of right now by going out in the back yard and looking around at the earth, the lawn, the beds, the trees. The power of a mysterious thing called life, as revealed this month in living nature, can, if you see it intelligently, make all the combined powers of man look pretty frivolous.

Down on the ground at your feet, within the one glance of your eyes, are a million fragile green pins. They are the new grass, so tiny, so fragile, so utterly weak you wonder the breeze does not destroy them. Up out of the beds, poke the tender nebs of what will soon be garden plants. So delicate, a raindrop should shatter them. On each tree,

continued

a million buds in every one of which the infant leaves are more delicate than the frailest tissue paper.

In the robin's and sparrow's nests, eggs of a fragility for which there is no synonym. And in a week, nestlings, naked, too feeble to raise their heads, eyeless, ghastly in their weakness.

But in a stupendous rush, the power of life within four weeks will have transfigured every living thing, every tree, every blade, every flower, every bird, every creature, into a force of radiant, raging, triumphant life that should leave us speechless in our humility.

Pins

"See a pin, pick it up,
All day you'll have good luck."

Muttering this, I stooped and picked a pin off the pavement.

"What's this?" demanded my companion, who is a man of style and dignity.

I explained, while sticking the pin under the lapel of my coat.

"Luck," I said.

"For Pete's sake," he protested. "Picking a pin up off the dirty pavement. It is probably filthy. Hundreds of people have stepped on it. It has been kicked and squished around in the litter and muck of the pavement."

"Well, it's an old saying," I pleaded. "My grandmother

taught it to me. It is part of ancient wisdom, I imagine."

"Luck!" scoffed my companion. "You blocked traffic when you stopped and bent down. You were lucky not to be bunted onto your face, on a crowded street like this."

"Somebody has to keep alive the old superstitions," I suggested.

"Why?" enquired my companion loftily. "And besides, it isn't dignified in a man of your age to be seen picking pins off the street like that. What would people think of you? Suppose somebody knew you and saw you pollacking pins?"

"I'm sorry if I embarrassed you," I apologized, and, humbled, I cast my eyes down. I saw another pin, a lovely new one, shining. I fought furiously, but nothing could restrain the familiar impulse. I fell back slightly and stooped.

Overhead, on the front of the bank building we were passing, a man was cleaning off a pigeon's favorite window ledge and missed the pail he was holding. The litter fell precisely on my friend's hat and shoulders. It would have hit me too, if I had been obediently beside him.

While he was in discussing the matter with the bank management, I stood outside, remembering my grandmother.

The Lender

There is an ancient saying: "Never lend money to a friend for then you will lose both."

A wealthy old boy of my acquaintance has given this a special twist.

"The best way to get rid of tiresome people is to lend them money," he says. "For instance, how did I know I was going to be so well off? You make friends, when you are young, with some people who turn out to be so different from what you thought they would be. I had one bosom friend in my twenties who, in his thirties, joined one of those fanatical small religious sects that became an obsession with him. He was so darn good, and honest, and my friendship with him was so long established that I didn't know how to deal with him. For he plagued the life out of me, trying to convert me to his new faith which was as deeply obnoxious to me as it was precious to him. By sheer good luck, he got into difficulties, and I was able, even then, to lend him $1,000. I have hardly seen him since. And that was twenty-five years ago.

"Take relatives," he said. "Blood is thicker than water, surely. Now, my wife, who turned out to be a bit of a pain in the neck after we were married twenty years or so, can't stand my relatives. Never could. We had one set of relatives who, when I started to make money, rejoiced in coming to stay with us in our first big home. They would stay for a week, two, three weeks. They simply took us over as their fortunate relations. To them it was the most natural thing in the world that they should visit us at regular intervals and have a whale of a time. I thought my wife would go crazy. She was going to leave me. Well, I wouldn't want to have to go through all the trouble of finding and adapting myself to any more women, so I was overjoyed when my relatives asked me if I would lend them a quite substantial sum as down payment on a new house they wanted to buy. You bet I would.

"That was the last of them, except at family weddings and funerals, of course. They have never been back for a nice long visit. How could they, when they still owe me all the money, plus interest, of which my bank keeps reminding them, periodically, as a matter of mere routine."

A cold-blooded old man? Perhaps. But there are few of us who haven't got acquaintances we would like to lend $1,000 to.

The Owl

A long-eared owl is not a particularly rare creature, but it is certainly an exciting and bizarre thing to come across in a swamp, sitting there cuddled up to the cedar trunk, and trying to look like a rag of loose cedar bark. With its absurd long ears, like Mephistophelean eyebrows, quivering and erecting, and its irate eyes glaring, it is an

continued

embodiment of indignant nature. Owls, you understand, should be heard and not seen. And no lady caught in the corridor with only a towel around her could be more outraged than an owl with a bunch of human beings looking at it.

Our party made a lot of tracks in the snow as we gathered from all parts of the swamp to see the owl. And no doubt some curious farm boy, passing later, saw the beaten snow and went in to investigate. Where the party had assembled was well trodden. And no doubt the farm boy, using his normal Sherlock Holmes faculties, discovered the owl in the cedars.

The next party, to whom we gave directions how to locate the owl, arrived the next day and found it, all right. It was lying dead on the snow under the cedars, with a .22 bullet through its breast.

Our indignation at the death of this harmless, useful owl no doubt varied in its intensity depending on the purity of love for the animal world of each of those among us. Mine would be exceeded by the indignation of the truer nature lover who sees the handsome buck draped over my car fenders as I drive proudly home in November. And that person's indignation is probably only exceeded by that of a vegetarian, who sees her neighbor carrying home a parcel of lamb chops from the butcher's. Dear, dear little lamb.

It would appear we are all cranks. We have our loves and hates, each of which we are prepared to protest and defend with our lives. Maybe the lady who saw me bringing home an antlered buck hoped I would choke to death on a jagged fragment of my own bullet. All I hope is that the farm boy who shot the owl will get the hives.

Night Club

Some friends took me to a night club, thinking to give the old gentleman a taste of high life, and a glimpse of what goes on behind his pious old back.

It was down cellar. The only light in which you could see was over the hat check girl's counter. From there in, gloom. It was like a funeral parlour with only the night-light on. I supposed we were in a passageway until my ears told me there were people all around me; and then, my friends steering me by the elbow, I dimly perceived the place was full of ladies and gents seated at low tables, or slumped against wall settees, their cigarettes winking.

By the time my eyes accustomed themselves to the gloom, I could see waiters in red jackets stalking about like undertakers' assistants, keeping a melancholy eye on the mourners.

With a frightening yell, a female singer was suddenly lept, as the Irish say, into a dazzling spotlight, and what is called a combo of three bashful-looking musicians, heads bent, blew their horns, plucked their horse fiddle and their gitter, and made a deafening racket for over forty minutes. The girl singing would have got the hook at any amateur contest in my day.

On the way out, I leaned over the counter and whispered to the fat pretty hat check girl:

"Why do they keep it so dim down there?"

"If they could see one another, Pop," she whispered back, "they'd give up drinking."

Veracity

To newspapermen, one of the commonest and most amusing forms of snobbery is to be found among the would-be gentry of our day and age who detest the press. One of the readiest ways of indicating you are a lady or a gent is to express on all occasions your detestation of the press.

I ran into one of these ladies who asked me if I had noticed her picture in the paper the other day. It was on some social occasion at which the lady was in the chair, speaking.

"I begged the press photographer," assured the lady, "not to take any photographs. I begged him. I asked him not to pop off any of those nasty little flash things. I detest them. But he went right ahead. And you should see the result! I look like a hen cackling!"

Now, until that instant, I could not, for the life of me, think of what this lady reminded me of, as she chattered to me. But there it was, a hen cackling. In fact I never saw a more startling resemblance.

This is offered as proof of the honesty of the press.

Noisy and Captive

The wild creatures man has long ages ago tamed for his own use are the barking dog, the cackling hen, the bawling cow, the squealing pig, the whinnying, loud-footed horse.

It was the noisy animals that fell prey to primitive man's lasso and pitfall. All the silent animals are still wild, still free. The list can be increased. The endlessly cooing pigeon, the bleating sheep, the honking goose, the quacking duck. Among all the slaves man has made among the animals, hardly one is mute.

The noises these creatures made doubtless had something to do with their ease of capture. When the foolish wild hen, excited over laying an egg, began her hysterical cackling in the jungle, it was no trick for the cave wife, finding a nest, to wait until the chicks were hatched and then carry them into the cave. Poultry were likely our first livestock.

The wild cow, bawling in the primeval meadows, drew the hunters to find what a stupid, easily roped creature she was. The dog yapping, the hog squealing, all the destined slaves of man had the trick of revealing their whereabouts, and the location of their young, to be carried home and penned.

A dog is just a wolf that yapped too much and too near

continued

man. The wolf that stayed is the one that never howled until he knew he had two valleys and three hills between him and the nearest man.

There is some kind of a moral in this for humans. Are talkative, cackling people more enslaved than the glum, quiet type? Are people who squeal, honk, quack, yap and whinny more penned than the mute, silent, strong type? It is hard to decide, for some of the most successful men I know are blatherskites; while others watch their words as if they were dollars, and are just as liberal with them.

Keys

Right among us today are any number of people who can remember easily the day when you never carried the house key on you. There was only one proper place for the house key, and that was hanging on a string inside the letterbox or else under the doormat at the front door.

Not the occasional home, but nearly every house had its key on a string. Inside the door, just above the letterbox was a tack. Tied to the tack was a string two or three feet long to which the key was tied. When you came home, you curled a finger in the letterbox and got the key. If it wasn't there, you lifted the doormat with one foot and picked up the key off the veranda floor.

There were, I must admit, a few peculiarly suspicious families that had other hiding places for their keys: the milk box, or up on a little cornice on the veranda. But we always looked on these people as being a little odd.

These days were not so far off that we did not have automobiles. Because I can distinctly recollect that nobody ever took the car key out of the car unless there were some mischievous boys living down the street. Then you would remove the car key before retiring for the night and leave the car in the side drive. But out in front of your house, or shopping up at the corner, or even downtown, you never took the car key out. Why should you?

There came the day, however, when the police had to utter and publish a warning to the public, advising them, almost apologetically, to remove the car key. A few years later, the police made it an offense to leave your key in the car.

It must have been about this same time that the string was taken down off the inside of doors, over the letterbox, we stopped leaving the key under the doormat. And now today everybody has a house key, and keeps it privily in purse or pocket.

But the exciting thing, the wonderful thing is that it was within easy memory, it was only a little while ago, that the world was so simple and trusting. What a queer change in one generation. Ours!

Subtle

An advertising man who used to go fishing with me until he got too prosperous to go fishing anywhere but in the deep sea off the costliest coasts of North and South America and New Zealand had me for a ride in his new European sport car, and we ended up at his magnificent home twenty miles beyond the city's most vulgar limits.

He is sloshing in money. And as we sat in his gracious living room graciously living, recollecting old fishing trips and remembering the days when we used to lend each other five bucks every other week, I asked him to what, above all, he owed his remarkable success.

"The word subtle," he replied.

"The word?"

"Subtle," said he. "Twenty years ago, when I was a young and struggling copy writer, I used to write a piece and take it in to my boss, the head of the copy department, who was also a vice-president. He would read it and look at me. I was watching him with an expression of intense expectation. It's so subtle, I would explain, that it takes minutes to get it. The average reader, I would point out, would miss the subtlety entirely and be sold. Ha! he would say, suddenly. And together we would go and see the client. We would both sit, watching with that air of expectancy, while they read it. Get it? we would cry.

"Ah, yes, yes. Subtle, we would point out.

"In two years, I was the subtlest guy in the agency. In five years I was vice-president. Subtle. It means you can't really see it. It's there, but you can't see it. None of them ever saw it; so now I'm the president."

Exchange

Lap Laprairie who is widely known amongst Canadian construction men from Kittimat to Knob Lake as an outstanding authority on explosives has a most interesting story about Indians. When he was a young man, Lap was on a construction job far in the north where the white man had seldom penetrated before. A construction camp was built and the crews came in and work was begun in the wilds.

The construction crews were surprised to find, here and there, snowshoes hung on trees, or bags of traps and other interesting items of wilderness gear. Even rifles were discovered, wrapped in coverings, but quite openly hung in trees. The white men promptly appropriated these goods, on the principle of finders keepers.

The white men did not know that Indians, as a matter of course, left their property wherever convenience or necessity required, and that to an Indian it was unthinkable that anyone would disturb property that was not his own. The things they left in the woods were, of course, vital to them: the owner's existence depended upon them in most cases. The theft of them was a profound shock to the Indians.

Then the Indians perceived that the white man's principles were different. The white man took what he wanted.

continued

Therefore he must expect the Indian to take what he wanted. And what was at first supposed to be theft by the Indians began to be noticed around the camps and on the trails and roads. But the Indians did not deem it to be theft at all; it was fair exchange, on an interesting new principle introduced by the white man.

It would be as hard, says Lap Laprairie, to make an Indian understand that he was to submit to the removal of his goods without being entirely free to remove the white men's goods, as to make a white man understand that he couldn't pick up and take away something he found hanging on a tree in the bush.

One of the tragedies of the white man, lately demonstrated all over the world, is that when he enters strange foreign territory, he rarely stops to think.

The Loosener

One of our eminent businessmen has the habit of scratching his head and rumpling his hair whenever he is puzzled. His associates are familiar with it as one of his ingrained habits. Sometimes he will scratch his chin, or even reach inside his jacket and scratch his chest. He is a scratcher.

On TV recently, he was on a panel, and no sooner was the program nicely started than he began scratching his head and rumpling his hair. Almost as if by magic, the whole panel of men were relaxed and in a good humor.

I mentioned this to him a day or two after.

"Oh," he laughed, "that's deliberate. That is an affectation. I learned it from a dog."

This called for the story.

"When I was a young fellow," he said, "I owned an old Airedale that was an awful character. And whenever I scolded him, he would listen in respectful dismay for a moment, then suddenly sit down and start industriously scratching. In whatever embarrassment he found himself, he solved it instantly by indulging in a good scratch. There is something disconcerting about a scratch.

"Next time my father bawled me out, I started to scratch my head. I was astonished to see my father promptly disconcerted, and the lecture died out. When I got into business, whether being cussed out by my superiors or in some predicament with my fellow workers, I found a good scratch seemed to bring everything down to earth at once. It is homely. It is impolite, but it is homely.

"In the army I was up for court martial for slapping a sergeant around. Standing before the court, I suddenly reached in and scratched my shoulder. The sergeant of the guard roared. The officers stared at me shocked. When you've got to scratch, I said, firmly, you've got to scratch. I was let off with a very light sentence.

"It is psychological. On the TV panel, I felt we were all sitting there as stiff as pokers and full of self consciousness. So, I scratched. And sure enough, everybody at once relaxed."

Friday Night Fervor

Symphony concerts and prize fights have this in common: they both vastly increased their audiences after TV came in.

In former times, one crowd went to the symphonies. Another crowd took in the fights. Then it got so you couldn't single out one crowd from the other. I have a bull-necked, thick-headed friend who had never heard a chord of symphony music but who knew who knocked out whom in which round in what town in what year, in every weight division for forty years back. Then his daughter secretly became an addict of hi-fi and had a tailor-made one installed in the rumpus room. My friend so fell for Tchaikowsky that he could soon even swallow Shostokovitch.

I went over to see him. And if you can imagine anything worse than watching a prize fight on TV to the overwhelming sounds of Brahms piano concerto number two, then you understand what was happening to the world of art. Referring of course to the manly art.

On the other hand, I am on terms of family relationship with a minister's widow and a minister's daughter. They both led a very sheltered, indeed, a genteel life. I doubt very much if they knew what prize-fighting was, for it was considered unmaidenly and unwomanly to look at the sporting pages of the newspapers. Those, like cigars, were for the men.

Well, their decline set in when they got a TV and they

were introduced to hockey. To hear their voices, attuned more to hymns and psalms, screaming at a goalie or berating the referees in fine vestry English, was something. But, in due time, to hear them when a fight developed on the ice, was something more.

I feel sure at first they most fastidiously avoided the prize fights. But, I regret to say, they were watching them. It is true they watched at first with expressions of dismay and obvious disapprobation.

But that is how they first viewed hockey and when in the fullness of time the Friday night fights left the air there was obvious regret in our household.

Intrusion

In late September when the cottages are shuttered and quiet, the roads all but deserted, the lakes and streams empty of the racket of outboards and boats, what do you suppose the wild things think of it? For two months of the year, the peace and stillness which so becomes their world for the other ten months of the year is suddenly invaded by the noisiest of all animals, man. And then, for no reason apparent to a wild mind, man vanishes as though chased, pursued or driven away.

Our intrusion comes at a particularly bad time, from the wild nature's point of view. The birds are barely through nesting. The young fox and raccoon and deer are not yet

continued

out of their mothers' care. All the minor characters of the drama, mice, bats, squirrels, have got the world decently apportioned amongst themselves, when, bingo, the sky echoes with a sudden clamor; there is banging and chopping; engines roar, strange voices pierce the day and night; the air is filled with fumes, the water fouled with oils. There is no privacy any more, and odoriferous monsters on only two legs come poking and peering into the secret places.

As suddenly as they came, these disturbers of the peace vanish. The birds, probably, suppose we are a migratory species like themselves. They figure we have come and nested and gone back south with our young. The raccoon, exploring eagerly around our cottage back doors and sniffing all cracks, surmise we came up here to get something, and that we have got it and taken it away, possibly leaving one small portion of it behind in our hasty departure. And for that he will just have a little look around. The fox, heaven and the mice alone, will know what a fox thinks. But he stands at a discreet distance, wrinkling his nose and saying good riddance. The air is cleaner now. In another couple of weeks, not even he will remember that we were there.

The Unmuzzled Saint

In all our cities and most of suburbia, Santa Claus is heard in season braying, ho-ho-ing and singing his infernal ditties out of store windows and from other points of vantage and surprise—a malevolent old demon in white whiskers and scarlet bulges beckoning the dear little children to him.

Santa Claus originally was a secretive sort of fellow. Not only did nobody ever see him. You weren't even supposed to hear him. He came in stealth in the middle of the night. So intent in not being visualized was he that he came down chimneys instead of using doors or even windows. A more elusive and invisible character did not exist. He was such stuff as dreams are made of, and you were only to see him in your dreams.

Then along about the three-quarter pole of the last century, somebody, probably a merchant or a salesman, got the idea of dressing up as Santa Claus in his own house, and entertaining his children. The idea spread like wildfire. Santa Claus suits and beards went on sale everywhere. By 1900, a daddy who wouldn't dress up as Santa Claus early Christmas morning wasn't worthy of the name.

But just about the time every house on the street had an old Santa Claus outfit stowed away with the Christmas tree decorations, the stores got the idea of removing the old gentleman from the domestic to the mercantile sphere. And there he is today, dozens of him in every city, as

continued

competitive an old boy as ever came out of mythology.

The conversion of Santa Claus from the most elusive and ethereal into the most solid and multiple of figures, all within two generations from a soundless wraith into the noisiest guy in history stands as quite a feat of social engineering.

What You Can Read in a Stump

One of the small exciting things going on around us of which we have little or no awareness is the routine research being done by people like foresters. In a letter from the forestry district of Parry Sound, Ontario, there is given the detail with regard to a hemlock tree which was cut with too tall a stump to please the forestry boys. They like the lumbermen to cut the forest as close to the ground as possible, and not waste good timber.

Foresters can read a tree stump as if it were pages of history. By the number and size of rings in the growth of the log, they can count every year of a tree's life. But more than that, they can, from the size of these rings, tell the years of famine and feast in that tree's lifetime.

The hemlock tree they took for their example was born from the seed in the year 1746. This tree was only fifteen inches in diameter at the butt in 1956. When it was born,

George II was on the throne and Bonnie Prince Charlie had been defeated at Colloden only one year before. Maybe the very year the hemlock seed fell into the earth. The French Revolution had not occurred, neither had the American.

This hemlock, little more than a foot through, was 200 years old. Here is what the foresters read: in the hundred years from 1746 to 1846, the tree grew only to a size of two and a half inches at the butt. Just a slender tent pole of a hemlock but a century old. The foresters figure that in those hundred years it was overshadowed by greater trees that starved it and retarded its growth.

Between 1846 and 1922, the hemlock suddenly put on a remarkable spurt, and in the seventy-six years grew from that tent pole into a handsome big hemlock with a diameter of twelve and a half inches.

From this, the foresters deduced that, either by blowdown in a storm, or from some other cause, the trees that overshadowed our hero had been removed, and it had a chance to flourish. By 1922, it was sufficiently the master of its immediate area that it put on another spurt, and in the thirty-four years to its death, it laid on the rings so fast that it reached fifteen inches in diameter at the stump.

The lesson for us greenhorns is that a small tree is not necessarily a young tree. Maybe it is older than your grandmother.

Twenty-Two . . . Helloo

My friend Wallace wants me on the telephone, so he says to his switchboard girl, "Get me Greg Clark." The girl calls me and says "Hold the line please."

Meanwhile, Wallace has just thought of something and steps outside his office to speak to a fellow big-executive.

I start to count, "One, two, three, four, five . . . " By the time Wallace hears his own phone ringing and suspends his conversation with the fellow big-executive, I have counted, slowly, up to twenty-two.

When Wallace picks up his phone, his switchboard girl informs him "Here's Mr. Clark." And Wallace hears me starting to count all over again—"one, two, three, four . . . " And while Wallace yells "Hey, hello, what's going on?" I resolutely keep on counting, eleven, twelve, thirteen," and so on until I reach twenty-two, which is exactly the time Wallace, for his own convenience, kept me sitting with my telephone to my ear. For I will be hanged if even my friends, let alone perfect strangers, are going to pull this ill-mannered trick on me.

What few, if any, faults are still to be found with the modern telephone system are generally to be credited to the subscriber.

The Sting

A fox terrier is not as a rule my fancy of a dog. He is not relaxed enough. He has too much to say. I like a reflective dog, like a hound. But one fox terrier of my acquaintance has my sympathy and even though it is hilarious sympathy, it is deeply felt. What happened to this terrier shouldn't happen to a dog, and especially not to a dog of a stump-tail variety.

The terrier came into our boat house to check things over, as fox terriers do. On the ceiling is a small hornet's nest, about the size of a tennis ball. We ignore it, and it ignores us, beyond an occasional angry zoom on the part of a hornet now and again, whenever we make too much noise.

The terrier spotted the silver-grey nest, with the three or four hornets lazily taking off and landing around it. With an easy bound, the dog leaped on an old table that stands below the nest, in order to have a closer look.

A hornet dropped down and made a warning zoom around the terrier, who promptly snapped at it. There is one part of a terrier that distinguishes him: his valiant, stubby tail, always erect, always wagging. Most dogs wag their tails out of sheer friendliness. This is not quite so of a fox terrier. He wags his as a pennant, a gauge, a challenge. It is a signal of his high and eager spirit.

The hornet, missed by the snapping jaws, immediately

continued

landed on the very tip of the lively tail. And promptly sank his red hot prong into what might be the most sensitive square inch of a dog's whole anatomy.

With a screech that started not in his throat, not in his chest, but from his hind quarters so ear-splitting was it, the fox terrier leaped from the table. He barely touched the boat house floor as he soared out the open door. Once outside, he fell for the ancient delusion which dogs dogs—that they can bite their tails. He was just a blur as he spun like a pinwheel, emitting the most frantic howls and coloratura cadenzas. Realizing that he was not gaining on his tail, he changed tactics, and began a series of the most colossal bounds a fox terrier ever took, trying to leave his tail behind him in one merciful and stupendous leap. Finally, he leaped in the water, and there we retrieved him and put mud on his stump. He has been a very reflective terrier lately, around our boat house.

Rising Seventy

As you begin to rise seventy, you begin to believe again in imps, sprites and fairies. You have to. The evidence begins to accumulate, as it did in your childhood, that there are mysterious personages in this life beyond the realm of vision. And, like the companion gnomes of childhood, they are mischievous.

For example, I had to mail a money order to the States. So I prepared a letter, addressed an envelope, stuck a stamp on it, and carefully leaving the flap unstuck, I put it in my wallet. Thus, all I had to do on obtaining the money order at the bank, was put it in the envelope, seal and mail.

Fine. Everything went as planned. I took the money order from the girl, reached in my wallet, removed the letter. And do you know what? The envelope was sealed.

No, sir, Not accidentally. It was sealed as solidly as if I had myself licked it. Who did it?

Some imp, what else?

A thousand other evidences pile up. I lock the door at bedtime and turn off the porch light. In the morning, believe it or not, the door is unlocked, and the porch light is still on. I hang my coat in the closet and an hour later, there it is where somebody, and you know who I mean by somebody, has taken it out of the closet and thrown it carelessly on the sofa.

Somebody, and I bet he isn't three inches tall, puts an extra step in the hall stairs; or worse, takes one out. Hides pens, wrist watches, hats, gloves, shoes. Changes the position of light switches on the wall, so you can't find them in their usual place.

Indeed, it is amazing the places you find things, when you are rising seventy.

The Purple Aster

Leaving Prestwick in Scotland to fly to Montreal, I picked a small purple aster from the flower border at the airfield and put it in a little silver gadget I wear in my lapel, with water in it, for keeping posies fresh.

A small incident occurred on the flight which is of no importance to my story, but the radio men were at the airfield in Montreal to interview us passengers, and when my time came to address the mike, all I could think of to say that, whatever else might be wrong with the journey, it was short enough, for did I not have in my lapel, as fresh as the morning, a little purple aster I had plucked in Prestwick a few hours ago.

When I got from the airfield to my hotel in Montreal, there were five Scotchmen waiting for me at the registration desk: tall, sandy, boney Scotchmen; short, wide, bandy-legged Scotchmen. They wanted that aster. Separately, unknown to one another, they had heard the radio and raced like mad to intercept me at the hotel. I told them that my wife was of Scottish descent, and I wished to wear the flower fresh another three hundred miles and give it to her.

When I got to my room, there was a phone call waiting—a gentleman named Cameron from Peebles, unknown to me. The bellhop came in while I was convairsing with Cameron, with six slips of paper with urgent telephone numbers on them. All Scotchmen I had never heard of. All wanting that wee aster, that gowan, that flure, they called it.

More came in person before I caught the night plane west. They had me paged at dinner. They knocked at my door. There were telegrams from the suburbs of Montreal and two long distance calls.

I refreshed the water in the little gadget; and with my bags piled into a taxi for the airfield.

"Ye wudna," said the taxi driver in a hoarse voice, "be the gentleman wha wore the. . . . "

"Here!" I cried. "Take it."

He took it as if it were the jewels of the Madonna.

The Scotch are a strange, great race.

The Planner

Another long summer has ended, and my cottage neighbor who plans had had a wonderful season. He has envisioned in his mind plans that excel anything that he has planned for years.

He owns a comfortable cottage set in a pleasant grove of pines and oaks, with sundry underbrush of saplings, ferns, wild asters and poison ivy. He has a wharf that has withstood the slings and arrows of the outrageous years

continued

and is only slightly sunken.

Each summer, he spends a most enjoyable time walking about his demesne, standing on the rocky point in front, surveying the cottage, the wharf and the woodlot. On rainy days, he sits on the veranda viewing the never-changing situation and making voluminous notes, with figured calculations and small drawings that embody the plans he has for the new wharf, the pretty little chalet type sleeping cabin up there on the slope. He plans to clean out the woodlot, slash away all the underbrush, cut down the ailing trees and convert it into a matchless little pine grove, singing in the wind. He has been planning now for twenty years, and he tells me the clarity, beauty and detail of this past summer's planning has given him the most enjoyable summer he can remember.

Lemmings

On my last visit to Hudson Bay, I met a biologist who, on holding out his hand to shake mine, deposited a live lemming in my palm. It was a beautiful little thing, twice the size of a mouse, with incredibly soft fur, looking to my mind like a tiny beaver rather than a mouse.

A little creature of deep mystery that dwells in superb prosperity in the iron Arctic and on whose comings and going much of the life of the Arctic depends.

"Such records as exist of the fluctuations of wild life in the Arctic tell of the effect of the lemming fluctuations on all life" John Howes writes. During the years preceding the lemming 'crash'[when occur in Canada those incredible marches of the lemmings to the north, to the sea and to destruction by the millions], falcons and hawks increase, snowy owls abound, foxes are numerous and refuse to be trapped. Wolverines, lynx, weasels and bears are found to be stuffed with lemmings. Wolves gorge themselves on the rodents. Caribou are absent from the lemming range, because the browse is poor, the moss riddled. When the lemmings move off, the countryside is in a sorry sight.

"Then the lemmings vanish, as with the snow. The falcon cliff becomes deserted. The snowy owl is no longer seen. The bears turn to berries, the wolves range far off after caribou. The Eskimo suffers from the absence of the wolf-driven caribou herds, but the trappers have one good season, when the foxes are hungry enough to take trap baits. Remarkable flights of snowy owls and goshawks make their appearance far to the south in Canada, even in the northern United States."

One strange feature of the lemming story is that in the middle ages in northern Europe, it was generally accepted that when the enormous hordes of lemmings appeared, prior to their death march, they had fallen from the clouds, and scientific writers of the time quoted witnesses to the rain of lemmings. To this day, in remote Eskimo lands it is their belief that lemmings dwell in the sky, and periodically come down in vast throngs in snow storms.

The Tracer

One of my backwoods cronies turned up in the big city to undergo a little surgery and I have had several conversations with him pinned to his hospital bed. He has many large and interesting ideas, the sort of ideas that come to a man out on the trapline or confined by the weather for a week at a time in a shanty far from the settlements.

Here, for instance, is my friend's suggestion as to how to deal with our bank bandits. He offers it freely to the police and to the Bankers' Association without anticipation of any reward.

"What you want," he says, "is a tiny little nozzle stuck through the counter in the bank, right under the teller's window. When your bandit hands in the usual note 'This is a stickup,' or pokes a gat through the wicket, the teller just pushes a button and out the little nozzle squirts a full size dose of skunk essence, fair in the giblets!"

I shook my old friend's hand and thanked him on behalf of the police and the Bankers' Association.

"You see," he went on, visibly pleased, "the trouble you have with these here bandits is, you can't identify them. They get out so quick and mingle with the crowd, as the newspapers say, that nobody can follow them or otherwise keep track of them. My system, you could trace the guy for about three days, if necessary."

I asked him, just for the record, what would happen to

everybody else in the bank. Wouldn't they all be picked up as suspects?

"Well, I thought of that," he explained. "You'd have to lock the bank doors and keep them all inside the bank for a few hours, until you had apprehended the real culprit, as the newspapers say."

I thought that perhaps the bank staffs, especially as there are so many young ladies on them, might not be altogether in favor of the scheme. And such bank managers as I have met would not perhaps be too keen on it either.

"Well," said my old crony, "I hate to see our good Canadian skunks left out of things. Nearly every other animal we got has some part to play. Porcupines, Indian baskets; frogs, frogs' legs; weasels, ermine. With a little imagination, a skunk, now. . . "

So we went on to his scheme for making Niagara run both ways, thus doubling its power potential.

Insufferable Asset

In a business office where I am obliged to call twice a month or so there is one employee whom I hate to encounter. He is a middle-aged man of a disagreeable and sour disposition. I try all sorts of dodges to be waited upon by other members of the office staff, all of whom are the most pleasant characters, man or woman, you

continued

would ever want to meet. But now and then, over the past ten years, I have had to deal with this insufferable gent; and the last time, I lost my temper and went in to see the boss.

All the time I was relating my grievance, the boss, who is an old fishing crony of mine, kept smiling more and more broadly.

"Sure he's a stinker," he agreed, when I finished.

"Then why do you keep him? The rest of the staff are such happy people."

"They are happy," said the boss, "because of him. You have to have one stinker in every organization for the sake of office morale. Give the rest of the staff somebody to hate, and they don't hate one another."

"You're kidding!" I protested.

"Not at all. It's a well-known principle of management," said the boss. "I would rather lose almost anybody out of the office rather than that old crab. He's worth his weight in gold."

"You're fooling. He's your wife's uncle, or something," I accused.

"No, sir," assured the boss. "Go into any well-run organization and you'll find the professional stinker, against whom all the rest of the staff are arrayed in loyal devotion to one another. As a matter of fact, I am having just the least little bit of bickering and jealousy among the girls lately. I am right now looking around for some choice battle-axe to add to the staff, so as to pull the rest of them together."

On my way out, I lifted my hat to the old stinker, much to his mystification.

Feeding Station

Ever since my boyhood, I have maintained some sort of bird feeding station in my back yard. As many as ten different species of wild birds, in the dead of winter, will come and share with the bawdy sparrows, starlings and pigeons what is daily spread for them on the sheltered shelf.

Forty or more generations of birds, therefore, many of them resident, have seen me come forth each day with my humble offering. But do they accept it as a gift? Do they get to know me and show some signs of trust and faith? Not them. Even at the glimpse of me through the kitchen window, they flash away with every expression of trepidation. Apparently in Nature, though you may tame the odd individual bird or squirrel or deer, there is no possible conception of a gift. What you get, you take.

The most comic manifestation of this is in the behaviour of the common blue jay. Not only does a blue jay not conceive of a gift—he wouldn't want it as a gift; he's got to believe he is stealing it. There is the feeding shelf, with its glass sides, and its wind-vanes steering it with the wind, on its pole. Around it are dozens of birds, feeding. In it, are whole peanuts and halves of walnuts in the shell, especially set out for the jay, since he is the only one capable of carrying them off.

A hundred feet away, he lands on a tree top and slyly edges closer and closer to the feeding station. With a swift dash, he is into the feeding station, snatches a nut and flies off with it, jeering.

I have known a great many men who were jay birds.

Twice each winter I buy about $15 worth of wild bird

continued

seed, concocted as follows according to the wisest authorities: There is millet and plain canary seed, sunflower and rape, cracked wheat and chick feed, and a nice warming infusion of buckwheat, dark, rich and shiny and guaranteed to hot up the innards of any frozen little bird. It is true the common sparrows, starlings and pigeons come to the feeding station and get most of it. But every so often, some fabulous stranger comes to the feast. And at current movie theatre and concert admission rates, the spectacle of thirty evening grosbeaks in the garden is well worth the cost, or even a chime of chickadees, on a wild, lone day.

But next to my yard is that of a lady who every day of her life distributes largesse in the shape of broken up bread scraps.

And what happens? Every sparrow, starling and pigeon in the neighborhood rushes to the feast, leaping up excitedly to leave my seed trays. With fury they fight over the bread, and not infrequently a lucky bird will fly over the fence with a chunk of it, to stage a battle with his brethren for the bread right amidst all my generously strewn seeds. It is disheartening.

But the baking industry ought to recruit a few million sparrows and starlings to testify on behalf of the dietary excellence of white bread.

One advantage accrued, however, to my feed trays. I noticed one day that while the sparrows, pigeons and starlings were over the fence rioting amid the bread crusts, a downy woodpecker came slyly in to feed on my suet container, three chickadees, grateful for the privacy, helped themselves on the seed tray, and one tree sparrow, lovelier than a painting by Fabricius, appeared magically amidst them.

The Practice of Fear

A dentist informs me that policemen give him more trouble than any other classification of his adult patients. The sight of forceps petrifies them. The drill reduces them to jelly. And this is reasonably so.

Policemen are not accustomed to being afraid. They are big men. In addition to their size and strength, they wear the added authority of the law. And, besides, they usually carry pistols or clubs. What is there for such a man to be afraid of?

Courage can be of two sorts. There is inborn courage. And then there is courage that comes of being entirely accustomed to fear. In two wars, the men I felt most sorry for were the big, hearty, fearless types who, in war, encountered fear for the first time and didn't know how to face it. Having, myself, been afraid of something or other all my life, being, at heart, a timid man, fear could never catch me unawares. Many a time I have been so scared I was unable to move a muscle. But, from long experience having been accustomed to the feeling, I was able perhaps to look a little less scared than I was. Certainly I was able to appear less frightened than a man who was frightened for the first time in his life. Thus, being unable to move, I got credit for being very nonchalant in the face of danger. Nonchalance is often paralysis.

But there is this to be said for the timid man who is accustomed to the sensation of fear: the paralysis is more quickly overcome, and something in the form of courage

continued

is the result. I had a sergeant in the first war who literally broke down with fright under shellfire. He became, for a few minutes, a dithering idiot. But then, with a sly grin, he would recover possession of himself, and become one of the deadliest, coolest, clearest-headed men I ever knew. It always happened. I witnessed it thirty or more times. He was a timid man, with the courage of the damned. He survived the war, and has run a little candy store now for thirty years.

Corporal James Post, D.C.M., was probably the most totally fearless man I ever encountered. After the battle of Passchendaele, in which action he won his decoration for climbing on top of a German concrete pillbox and dropping Mills bombs down its ventilator, I asked him if he wasn't scared clambering up in full view of the enemy all around.

"Sure I was scared," he said indignantly. "But no more scared than usual."

These truly brave men have a curious attitude towards fear.

Trap

A bee buzzing angrily inside a lady slipper orchid is one of the amusing sounds of small nature. It is a surprising sound, for, if the bee is a young one, not familiar with lady slippers, it can sound as mad as a rattlesnake. Bees are very sudden-tempered.

And lady slippers must have been very patient, over a few million years, to have worked out the mechanics of their reproduction so ingeniously as to entrap and infuriate bees.

All the lady slipper orchids are a beautiful and seductive color. They are either some shade of magenta and white, or else vivid yellow. No bee could miss seeing them. And on coming closer to inspect the color-signal, the way they zoom near you to check your red bandana, they sense the lovely aroma of nectar coming from the orchids.

To get into that sack from which the nectar odor floats, the bee, after exploring the impenetrable bauble, finds a crack through which he can shove his way; for the fissure is springy, and gives to pressure. Once inside the colored gloom, the bee is better than in clover, for the floor of the little balloon is covered with nectar-beaded hairs.

When the bee has his load of nectar and tries to get out, he finds that the springy door through which he entered is a trap door. What is more, the wall of his prison, on that side, is slippery as glass.

It is then he starts to buzz with fury. But in his anger, batting and banging around, he discovers a very small escape-hatch at the top of the bulbous prison. And the floor is good and rough, for a foothold up there. Out he goes, struggling, but in getting out, he first has to scrape his back along the stigma, which collects the pollen of previous orchids off his back; and then he has to heave his back against the mass of pollen in order to get through the escape hatch.

He forgets his anger; sees another orchid nearby; and with a practised eye, finds the fissure and bulges in. Possibly he gets mad again: for if you sit beside a lady slipper for a little while, you will hear a lot of anger.

Rocked

At the dinner table, I was lecturing my children and a couple of their guests on the sad decay of their generation. From the living room, where the ancient great-grandmother of the tribe eats her dinner by herself at a card table, so as not to miss the TV news, which is extremely important to her, came the loud rowdy sounds of a rock 'n' roll band playing and singing a piece called "Rock A Billy."

"When I was your age," I said above the din, "it was meaning, not sound, that appealed to us. Your generation is entirely infatuated with sound, beat, rhythm. Ours was a world of meaning. We sought meaning at the feet of our elders. In books. In our studies. Except in the big cities, there were no theatres; and even in the big cities, only three or four theatres that would hold a mere handful of the population. In the cities, as in the towns and cities, if you wanted music, you had to make it yourselves, at home."

The younger generation ate on.

"Church," I said, "was one of the places you could hear good music. But you also heard the sermon and passages of Holy Writ. I might say there was meaning in everything when I was your age. And the frightening thing is, it was only this one short lifetime ago, that all these revolutionary changes have come into being. Just listen to that racket!"

On the TV, the band, which comes on before the news,

was really rocking "Rock A Billy" and we could see Great-Grandma leaning forward to eat her dessert and also to inspect the TV screen more closely.

"Rock A Bill, Rock A Billy!" I chimed in scornfully.

"Daddy," said my daughter, "what does 'Yip-I-Addy-I-Aye' mean?"

"Mmm?" I asked, my mouth being full of beef.

"And what does 'Balm of Gilead, Way Down on the Ningo Farm' mean?" she pursued. "And then there's another you used to sing: 'Yoop-I-Dee-I-Day!' "

"That was a college song!" I protested.

"Well, okay. Then what does 'Yip-I-Addy-I-Aye' mean, or 'Ta-ra-ra-BOOM-de-ay.' What does THAT mean?"

The news suddenly came on, so I grabbed my dessert and hurried into the living room beside Great-Grandma.

I would answer them later, sometime.

Cutting Words

In June our Corgi is a little fat, the idleness and ease of winter not yet being absolved by the furious activity of summer. She will be a pretty dog in another month.

I had her out on a leash when a promenading lady paused to inspect us both. A lady of mature years and a masterful eye.

"Spayed, I suppose?" she said sharply.

continued

"Yes'm," I admitted.

"Anybody who would have a female dog spayed," she enunciated, "is little short of a monster."

Now, in cases like this you have to decide whether your assailant is a little cracked, or just a spoiled old hoot owl. I took a chance on the latter.

"Ma'am," I asked, "have you a fur coat?"

She glared in astonishment, but obviously she was the kind of lady who would have a fur coat.

"Shame on you," I declared.

On her hat was a bunch of ordinary feathers dyed a sort of mauve.

"Madam, do you know what feathers you are wearing in your hat? Those are rare trogen bird feathers, one of the most beautiful creatures of the Brazilian jungles!"

Speechless, she backed away and stamped up the street. I bet her menfolk caught the devil that night. Just to get even with the sex.

Psychic Signals

One of Canada's best hunters, anglers, and all-round field naturalists insists that there is a psychic force in nature that acts as a warning to all wild creatures when danger threatens.

On a recent fishing trip with him, I caught only four trout to his ten, though we fished side by side.

"You're too intent," he explained. "Your eagerness transmits itself to the trout."

"How?" I expostulated.

"Somehow," he replied. "I've seen it hundreds of times. Through your fishing rod, and down your line. Or through the air or water, like a radiation, an atomic radiation, maybe. . . . "

When you come to think about it, some of the most successful of your hunting and angling friends are phlegmatic types, easy-going, unexcited, calm. And some of the least successful are the most ardent, eager and devoted.

Later in the day, in a grove, we heard birds singing that might have been purple finches in their northern range, which have a special quality of song there, or it might have been some rarer bird of the finch family that we could not identify. We went ashore, separating to approach within binocular range of the singers. For me, they stopped instantly and flew away. And I had the experience of hearing them continuing in full, uninterrupted song while my languid friend walked right among them. They were warbling vireos, far north of their normal range.

"You sort of subdue yourself" my friend explained, "whenever you approach wild nature. And nothing is afraid."

Atomic energy may exert itself in more ways than in bombs.

Sleepers Arise!

A friend of mine has lately been obliged to start taking sleeping pills of the barbital group, which his doctor assures him are not habit-forming.

But they are habit forming. They form the habit of sleep. And when you consider how much of this little life is spent in sleep, the question arises: should it be encouraged? If a man lives to be sixty, and sleeps eight hours a day, then he has spent twenty years of his life unconscious.

In the first volume of his memoirs, Churchill describes how, in the early and desperate stages of the German blitz, he used to lie down for twenty minutes, right after lunch, and go into an immediate and deep sleep. From that twenty-minute cat-nap, he would wake as refreshed as if he had slept for hours, and carry on, full of vim, all through the rest of the day and far into the night.

Now, there is a system to be looked into. If we could work out a scheme whereby a man could lie down and have a snooze whenever he felt like it, the awful burden of sleep which has been imposed on mankind might be lifted. The way it is now, a tradition as ancient as the hills decrees that the night shall be spent asleep. This dates back to the cave man, doubtless, who, in the dark, had nothing else to do but sleep. So gripped are we by this tradition, that if we can't sleep at night, we go to the doctor for pills.

Other traditions are being demolished. Why should we not escape from the absurd and primitive tradition of sleep? Let a man sleep whenever he feels like it. Beside every office desk, beside every work bench and machine tool in the land, have a pleasant couch. And when he feels sleepy, the worker can lie down for a cat-nap, and awake full of vim. . . .

Of course, this would disarrange the eight hour day. We would have to adopt the twenty-four hour day, like Churchill.

Endangered Species: The Wild Game Provider

Two or three of my acquaintances are not going deer or bird shooting for the reason that their wives will no longer cheerfully prepare and cook the products of the hunt. And what is more, they are finding it harder and harder to find friends who will accept presents of game with any real enthusiasm.

The enormous improvement in the handling of food, particularly meat, during the past thirty years has resulted in a fast and steady decline in the popularity of game as a food. So immaculately clean, so appetizing to look at are the products of the modern packing industry and butcher business that the housewife today looks with horror on the shaggy and sometimes gory fruits of the chase, as they

continued

are handed over, wrapped in newspaper, by some genial sportsman of a neighbor or friend fresh home from the wilds.

Half the genius of the modern food industry is devoted to attractive packaging and presentation. There is nothing the sportsman can do to compare with that. He hangs his ducks or partridges on nails on the north side of the hunting cabin, day by day, until the hunt is over. He hangs his deer in the bush where it fell until the last day of the hunt, when the gang goes forth to carry the venison in.

The birds he stuffs in a carton to bring home in the trunk of his car. The deer, in pride, he drapes, antlers rampant, over the front bumper or fender of his car, where it gets the full heat of the engine for the long journey home. Better still, he might even rope the deer on the back bumper, where the exhaust pipe can fume it for a hundred miles.

While his friends bury their portions in the garden, the sportsman, using special sharp jellies and condiments such as currant jelly, wild grape jelly and spices, gloats over his traditional feast. And when the queer flavor exerts itself even through the condiments, he exults:

"Ah, that's the true wild game savor!"

Barrel Organs Could Help

When a city grows old enough to start modernizing itself, the city fathers should budget for a special small fund with which to buy twenty barrel organs and employ twenty elderly Italians to circulate in the downtown area playing their barrel organs from nine to five daily.

This, it seems to me, is the most economical device with which to offset the ghastly effects of modernization. Definitely, something has to be done to rescue a city from the brutality of contemporary architecture. Are we sea birds, puffins, gannets, that we are to be given those faceless cliffs upon which to perch?

Something homely, like barrel organs playing Tipperary in the canyons of business might save the situation. It need only be some little thing, like the miles of flower boxes along the ledges the architects put in Regent Street, London, when they remodelled it; or like the statues they secrete in unexpected places in Paris.

When a slum was wiped away in Paris and new slim, tidy streets of sleek apartments sprang up on the slum's site, there, at the entrance to the block, not ostentatiously, but slyly, sweetly, they built a shadowy niche and in it placed the small statue of a little slum child, thumbing his nose at the passers-by.

That was for remembrance.

The Drowser

Drowsing is a much more pleasurable exercise than sleeping. In sleep, we are unconscious. But drowsing allows us all the relaxed pleasure of sleep with enough consciousness, or intermittent consciousness, to permit us to enjoy the sensation of it.

Drowsing requires a certain slight amount of disturbance. Church is a good place to drowse, or riding on a train. The whole thing is spoiled if you fall asleep. That is why it is more difficult to drowse in winter than in summer. Drowsing in a deck chair in spring or summer, there are the sounds of street traffic, the bark of dogs, the disturbance of children to keep you hovering nicely. In winter, about the only thing we can depend on is the radio.

One of my friends who is practically a professional drowser is quite a connoisseur of radio programs suitable to drowsing. And he says the opera on Saturday afternoons, from the Metropolitan in New York are simply ideal for the purpose. In fact, he hurries home on Saturday in good time to get his shoes off and a quilt over him precisely as the curtain goes up on Act One of the opera.

He finds that, with the radio tuned down to just the right volume, the combination of orchestra and singers can be reduced to a pleasant mutter and mumble. The important thing is, that the arias arrive at precisely the right moments, nicely spaced every few minutes, so that either a soprano screeches or a tenor lets go a wild bugle note, which serves to rouse the drowser at the very instant he was about to spoil everything by falling asleep. He has no choice about the operas; Wagner is just as good as Verdi.

The intermissions come pleasantly, with the learned blather of the commentator or the quiz program, enough to wake the drowser to the point of going for a drink of water or a glance out the window. But then the curtain rises on the next act, and our drowser hurries to get snuggled for another forty minutes of beautiful hovering on the downy edge of slumber.

The Stare

We never know who is looking at us. Indeed, if we knew all the people who had looked at us, or noticed us, we might be flattered and proud, or mighty scared. It stands to reason that in the varied days of the long years, we have looked at countless people without knowing who they were. So countless people have looked at us. Great people, maybe, famous ones, statesmen, namely men, poets, leaders, criminals, thugs, heads of great enterprises.

In the elevator of a hotel the other afternoon, I shared it with one other. He was a large well-dressed man with a big, red moon face, ragged eyebrows and a pair of ice cold, large-pupilled eyes that had a kind of glare in them. I glanced at him, and found he was staring unblinking at me. I glanced aside. A moment later, I looked again,

continued

and he still was fixing me with a bold and somehow impudent stare.

"Are we acquainted?" I asked him sharply, and so unexpectedly that he was a little startled.

"I think not" he said, levelly, still staring.

"Then," I enquired hotly, "What are you staring at?"

He reddened angrily, and you could see he was not accustomed to being challenged for his arrogant stare.

Before he could figure out the proper smash rejoinder, the elevator door opened for my floor. And disengaging my glare from his, I strutted out.

Shortly after, going down on the elevator with the same boy at the lever, I enquired:

"Who was that big stiff I went up with a few minutes ago?"

"Well, he's one of the big operators in town here," said the boy. "He's some kind of a racketeer. You sure made him mad."

"Did I?"

"Yep. He told me he didn't know he was looking at anybody. He says he didn't even see you until you snapped at him."

"Hmmm," said I, heavily.

Woodland Homebodies

Naturalist William H. Burt says a bull moose will spend the entire year, apart from a little traipsing around in the mating season, all within a hundred acres of swamp. He has no curiosity about the world at large. He is entirely content with the food, shelter and security of an area smaller than the average farm.

The opossum, a curious animal if ever there was one even if he is without curiosity, has been found to spend its entire career, from birth to death, in an area of eleven acres.

Most of us go through our inquisitive lives without ever seeing anything of the teeming life everywhere around us in the mice, voles, moles, shrews and other abundant little mammals that are the principal inhabitants of the fields and forests that we imagine to be so still and devoid of life. Except when their furiously mounting population threatens them with starvation, and finally does destroy them by the millions in periodic "crashes," these small creatures also spend their entire lives in very small areas, believed in some instances to be measurable in square yards. The nest where they were born is the centre of their range, and they range very short distances from it in their whole brief lives.

Certain migratory mammals such as woodland caribou, like its immediate cousin the barren lands caribou, is what we might call a constant traveller. He has no true home,

continued

and from birth to death just wanders on, eating as he goes.

Wolves and foxes, being dogs, have a larger bump of curiosity than most animals, and are known to range widely. During a rabies scare in New York state, foxes trapped for examination were re-trapped twenty-five miles distant in three or four days. Trappers tell us that wolves in family packs will have a regular tour of their territory that will commonly take them in a twenty-five mile circle; and if persecuted they will move very great distances to new territories. But the homebody characteristic is true here too, for females will return, after a year's absence, to the neighborhood of their former dens.

A good home seems to appeal to animalkind as much as it does to mankind.

Among Those Present

I met Churchill five times, as nearly as I can recall. But it never took. The last time was in Ottawa when Churchill visited Canada in 1942 during the darkest days of the submarine menace. In accordance with one of the dopiest of rituals involving the great of this world, they took Churchill out to Uplands where, on a bitter, winter morning, he had to toddle through the slush and inspect a guard of honor of Air Force Erks.

Mackenzie King was slogging along slightly in rear of the dogged Churchill and he noticed me among the platoon of newspapermen scurrying along in their wake.

"Ah, Prime Minister," said King, "I'd like to present Mr. Clark, who accompanied me on my flight to Britain. . . ."

"Ah-jeh-doo!" said Churchill briefly over his shoulder.

I think neither Mr. King nor I made much impression on him.

Progress

One thing progress does not mean is comfort. It probably does mean convenience. Progress has given us a thousand gadgets. But a thousand gadgets is poor compensation for the confusion, fretting and jitters which progress has saddled us with. You take the little matter of getting packed up for a holiday. In my boyhood—and I am not so darn old—we packed all our stuff in trunks and a couple of dunnage bags, plus maybe a wooden box with handles on it for the bottled fruit and preserves, and then telephoned for the express man.

He called with his horse and wagon the night before our departure and took away the trunks and bags. And that was that. No more worry. Forget it. When we arrived at the cottage or the summer hotel the next day, there was our baggage sitting waiting for us. Comfort.

With nothing to carry but a couple of small valises, two or three fishing rods, a paddle maybe, sundry toys and a

continued

cardboard box with our lunch in it, we went comfortably down to the station and boarded the train. In perfect comfort, though possibly a bit cindery and certainly a little hot and sticky, we proceeded, with numerous interesting jolts, long halts, blowing of whistle and hissing of compressed air brakes, to our happy destination, where baggage and all else awaited us, sans touble, sans labor, sans lifting, hoisting, fumbling.

But see what progress has given us: the motor car. And into the motor car we toil and labor, carrying out the luggage and stowing it this way and stowing it that way. We sweat and strain, body all achin' and racked with pain, trying to get all the suitcases, heavy cartons of provisions, hatboxes, last minute paper bags, not to mention paddles, toys, pressure cookers and all the little items, stowed inside so as to leave room for the passengers. Is there comfort in this? Is there comfort in the thought, as we drive in the steaming traffic over the holiday highways, that all this junk will have to be unloaded when we get there, and carried laboriously up the hill to the cottage?

Let us preen ourselves on progress, of course. But don't let us delude ourselves that it is making us more comfortable. Progress is making us slaves of our gadgets.

Population Control—Natural and Assisted

On a small uninhabited island in the Niagara River, heavily wooded and very tangled, the government biologists detected the presence of deer that had apparently swum or, in a favorable instant, crossed on the ice of that turbulent river. Since nobody ever intrudes on the island and interference with the deer was likely to be at a minimum, the biologists seized upon the situation to make a study of survival.

In a year or two, the deer population had increased to more than a dozen. And after five years or so, the biologists made a sweep of the island, counting all the deer that doubled back past their line of drivers. There were more than a hundred.

Despite the abundant plant life and heavily forested character of the island, the biologists noted with concern that a great deal of the reachable browse on the island, the twigs and shoots of young growth, the branches of larger trees that were within reach of standing deer, had been eaten.

In spring, the biologists made a second thorough sweep

continued

of the island, and found the carcasses of fifty-two of the hundred deer, and on examination, all the dead deer were found to have died of malnutrition and starvation.

This confirms the experience in many areas in the United States, where the deer have been protected, and allowed to increase in such numbers as to overpopulate their feeding range. It is used to defend the sport of deer hunting, which should keep the deer population down within survival proportions. But the importance of the study lies in the light it sheds so dramatically on the processes of nature in balancing, invariably, the population of any wild life with its food supply. Nature plays no favorites. It defends its plants by starving the deer. It protects its rabbits by almost exterminating them and so starving the multiplied foxes. When the foxes are all but exterminated, the rabbits multiply.

Some years ago, an Indian friend of mine confessed to having set a fire that consumed thousands of acres of valuable timber.

"You white men," he said, "only want timber. I want deer and blueberries. They'll come after the fire. New growth."

I expressed my consternation.

"Who comes first? The white man or the Indian?" he enquired.

As an amateur naturalist, I didn't know the answer.

Nourishing Thought For June

If we were to go out to take off our hats to the vegetable kingdom now, it would be to the grass family we should make our first bow, and after that, the rose family.

The grass family gives us our wheat and other grains from which we make the staff of life. And to grass we owe the beasts we eat and those which serve us. The grass family gives us food and drink, the drink including milk as well as beer and malted liquor.

If the grass family gives us sustenance, it is the rose family that has offered us the finer things of life, and which might be credited with having done most, of all the vegetable kingdom, to civilize us.

For, to the rose family belong all our orchard trees, apple, peach, plum, cherry and pear. The raspberry and strawberry are both members of it. Surely it must have been on tasting these things that man, that meat-eating, bread-stuffing, beer-swilling creature, must have conceived the idea of being a gentleman.

To the rose also belongs the spiraea which gives the bridal look to June all across the country.

In the woods, besides the wild rose, the briar, the swamp and pasture rose, there are such members of the family as the queen-of-the-prairie, all the cinquefoils, the dalibarda and the tall hairy agrimony, which can be

continued

brewed for tea, and which served as a pot herb to our ancestors.

When we think of roses, our minds leap at once to that creature of the family we have brought to perfection in a hundred colors and shapes by floriculture over many centuries of love and labor.

It is merely the queen of a family to which humanity owes half its everyday delights.

The Hamper

For thirty years, a lady of my acquaintance has been bringing a succession of cats with her up to her summer cottage in a sturdy wicker hamper. This hamper has long been familiar to the deckhands on the steamer that serves her summer resort and to the local settlers who do the baggage delivery and that sort of service.

This year the lady decided not to bring any cats or animals with her, because her cottage had been newly painted and she wanted to do some decorating. But she had the old hamper all cleaned and varnished and sent it up with the rest of her trunks and dunnage bags to be used as a picnic hamper, for which it was ideally suited.

The lady arrived two or three days later than her baggage. When she stepped off the steamer, the local settler ran up to her in great distress:

"Your cat," he announced, "was not in the hamper

when it arrived. The steamer people have hunted all over the place, enquired at all the other stops. . . . "

"But . . . " protested the lady.

"The railroad people," went on the agitated settler, "swear the cat was in the hamper when they delivered it to the steamer dock. One of the railroad men fed and watered it. And the steamer men swear the cat was in the hamper when they put it off here."

"But . . . " tried the lady again.

"I picked that hamper up," asserted the settler, stoutly, "within three minutes of it being put off the steamer, and there was no cat in it!"

"You see . . . " began the lady.

"I've searched all over this place," concluded the settler, "but nary a sign of the poor thing."

"Listen," insisted the lady. "There was no cat in it. I shipped the hamper up empty!"

Buck passing can still be done when there is no buck to pass.

Earthquake Drill

My grandmother was very fore-handed. When she read of the San Francisco earthquake, she promptly took steps to safeguard her own ménage from the effects of a similar disaster.

The first thing she set up was an earthquake reserve of

continued

food on the top shelf of the pantry. A bag of flour, tinned meat, salt, sugar and other staples, packed in sturdy containers and ready for emergency were stowed with instructions to everybody in the house that these were never to be touched.

In the attic, figuring that attic ruins would be on top of the rubble, she filled a trunk or two with earthquake emergency clothing. All the old heavy sweaters, footwear and underclothes were pinched from their familiar cupboards and marshalled in the attic trunks against the emergency. She filled a tin biscuit box with candles, bandages, medicines, pills. This trunk was never to be disturbed.

Her solution of the water problem was the masterpiece. In the accounts of the San Francisco disaster, she read of the broken water mains and the dread of contaminated water. Grandma had us all into the dining room for a lecture.

"Now if there is an earthquake," she commanded, "nobody, under any circumstances, flush the toilet. That tank of water above the toilet will be all that stands between us and death by typhoid."

"How about that boiler in the kitchen?" asked one of her daughters.

"You can't drink bath water," retorted Grandma, indignantly.

Water intended for the bath and bath water were the same thing to her. One of her irreverent grandchildren wrote a sign for the toilet tank: "In case of earthquakes, do not flush." Grandma died, full of years; no earthquake came; the pantry iron rations vanished; the old trunk was salvaged by the Red Cross. But sometimes in the night, when the national news bulletin is grim, we wake and remember Grandma.

Lines

Anybody can act on the radio, because he can hold the script right in his hand and never miss a syllable. But in television the actors have to learn their lines, as on the stage. It is true that on television, and in filmmaking, unlike the stage, you can use a blackboard and write out the lines or the speech a performer has to make in large print, and set it just out of sight of the camera so that it can be read by the actor. But these are aids, not substitutes, for memory when it comes to giving an authentic performance, as the tenderfoot is quick to discover.

Lately, I have been obliged to appear in a small part in a documentary motion picture, in which I had to learn as much as seven lines. I found it most extraordinarily difficult memorizing them. Poetry you can memorize, because it is cut nicely into stove wood lengths, with rhymes on the ends, like little bells to tinkle in your memory. But plain prose is very hard to memorize, especially unenlightened prose, like a commercial, or like this.

On the set with me were several professionals who, after one glance at the script, performed what seemed to me a miracle of memorization. They had it perfect in one try. I "fluffed" as they call it, three times, so that the camera had to grind my part out over and over.

In self-defense, I merely said that actors found it easy to memorize, because they had nothing much else on their minds. At the conclusion of the filming, the actors went home in one taxi, and I went in another. One must be very particular in figuring out excuses for one's self.

The Pipe

A happily married couple of my long acquaintance are facing a sad development in their relationship. A year ago, the husband developed a troublesome cough which started in the summer and continued all through the autumn and winter, without surcease. The cough became a domestic nuisance, the poor man barking and whooping from morning till night. The doctor treated him for bronchitis, and when that failed, a variety of other itises were explored, all in vain. The final conclusion was that the cough was simply and purely a cigarette cough.

So, face to face with the facts, the husband manfully adopted his wife's suggestion that he give up cigarettes forever, and take to a pipe.

This he did, to his delight and supreme satisfaction. The cough vanished and hasn't showed up again all the past year. The wife cheerfully resigned herself to tobacco leaking out of packages onto the chesterfields, and pipe ashes on the carpet, and piles of matches in every ash tray.

"But," she says, "it is awful, whenever there's a moment's silence, to hear him going pup-pup-pup all the time with that darn pipe. We have had to give up bridge. He's a slow bidder. And to have to sit there, with him going pup-pup-pup while he thinks what he will play next was driving me crazy."

I don't think they will actually separate; but I think they will spend their evenings, she down in the living room with the TV on loud, and him up in the den going pup-pup-pup.

Foxed

Two beagler friends of mine, Skipper Shanley Howard and Dr. Reg Paul, were out with their little hounds running a fox. But this fox was behaving oddly. Instead of running a wide course half way out of the township, it circled too briefly. So the doctor and the skipper walked over a few pastures and a couple of hills and, hearing the hounds coming, sat down on a hillside to watch the valley the fox was apparently returning to, time after time.

A minute or two ahead of the hounds came the fox, streaming by. Right below the watchers there was a hollow log lying in the brush. And into it the fox darted.

It waited only a moment, until the hounds were tonguing a couple of hundred yards away. Then the fox started out the other end of the hollow log, and away.

"Now why would he do that?" the sportsman wondered.

So they sat. And, in twenty minutes, round came the fox again. And again it started into the log for a moment; then, hounds nearing, out it popped from the far end.

Third time around, Dr. Paul exclaimed:

"There's two foxes!"

For they noted the difference in size and color. As one

continued

fox came in, the other fox, nicely rested, would pop out and carry on the chase. They were going to run the hounds ragged, by relay.

This account when originally published brought a furor of letters from fox hunters all over the country. Their tone was derisive. This was a matter of grief to Skipper Howard and Dr. Paul who told the story to the author. "So," says Skipper, "here's another. And any fox hunter who disbelieves this, simply hasn't ever been fox hunting."

When a fox gets weary of being run by the hounds, he simply runs in a circle and jumps.

He picks out a nice little copse or clump of brush with a stump or a rock in the middle of it. You will find plenty of such hummocks in old pastures and around the edge of woodlots.

Around this copse a fox runs not once but two or three times, leaving a good clear hot trail in a circle. A ring.

Then, with a colossal jump, the fox bounds as far as it can right into the middle of the ring. And there it sits on the stump or rock and waits for the hounds to catch up. They run around the circle. They run around it again. And again, furiously tonguing.

Now, it is the nature of hounds to run wide. So there they go, round and round, getting wider all the time, and farther out, with the fox sitting pretty in the middle laughing. And in a few minutes, the hounds have run so wide they have lost the scent entirely, and give up and go home.

Now how about that?

Early and Late Bloomers

It could be that people bloom, each in his or her season, like tulips, petunias, roses, zinnias. Some early, some in mid-life, some late. In the one ten-hour day I had a strange experience that suggests this. In the morning, I met and had lunch with an old friend who has been in California for the past twenty years. At college, he was not only the handsomest man for miles around, he was a great athlete, an intensely popular character and a companion of the greatest wit, humor and general intelligence. I suppose he was by ten lengths the most promising of our generation.

He bloomed young. He was a tulip, an early season organism, destined to flourish in a prime confined to possibly a ten-year period between the ages of twenty and thirty. He informed me, without any rancor or regret, that he had lost all his ambition in his mid-thirties and had got an insignificant job in a wholesale business and has been content to hold it ever since. I haven't had a duller lunch since the last time I ate alone.

In the afternoon, I went into a bookstore to try and get a book about J.J. Hill, the old-time railroad builder. The clerk hunted around on shelves and in publishers' catalogues and finally went behind into an inner office.

Out came a middle-aged woman, as strikingly beautiful a woman as you will ever see of middle-age; a magnificent head of white hair, lovely complexion, dressed like a fashion plate of a businesswoman, and a wide, friendly eye. Looking at me with an expression of recognition, she

continued

listened to my requirements, made notes, and said she would have a couple of books in a day or two. Then she asked me my name.

"Don't you remember me?" she asked.

I found not a wisp of remembrance.

"Why," she laughed, "I was in high school, in the same room with you. I was at university, in the same classes. . . ."

She told me her name. I had trouble keeping my balance for an instant. I remembered a slab-sided, homely dormouse, a shrinking, home-going, arms-full-of-books girl. . . .

She was a summer and autumn bloomer; asters, dahlias, zinnias.

Incunabula

I have never really wanted to know what incunabula means.

In the past fifty years, I have seen the word fifteen or twenty times. But there was something about it that did not appeal to me. I ignored it. I pretended I did not see it. I averted my mind.

It turned up in the strangest places. It was not one of those words you meet out in the bright light of day, so to speak, walking on the main streets, or in the stores, or even at home, sitting around.

No. It was up strange alleys, such as in catalogues of auction sales. It had a creepy Mr. Hyde look about it, as you would encounter it on foggy nights in a book about the authenticity of Shakespeare.

Incunabula. Incunabula! It is a word you cannot whisper. It is a word for mumbling or incanting. It has been, for about fifty years, the number one word I did not wish to know. Mind you, there are others like denigrate, superficies, glomerate. These are words I have ducked.

But just now I was looking up the dictionary to see what inchoate means. And there was incunabula! Just like all the other bogeys, a fraud.

"Works of an early epoch, specifically, books printed before 1501, A.D."

A lot of these cloak and dagger words are mere scarecrows.

Duped

According to the veterinary science, there is a certain amount of feeble-mindedness amongst animals. Now and again, a nitwit dog or horse is born, though the incidence is not as great as amongst the human species.

Yet in a litter of pups, there are all the degrees of mental agility that you will find in a family of human beings, some bright, some dull. Every breeder of sporting dogs, for instance, knows that in any litter you will find one

continued

or two dogs that are intelligent enough to absorb training. The rest are dopes. The good-looking ones might be developed as show dogs. What is left become pets. Just the same as in a human family.

A cocker spaniel with whom I am acquainted is a pretty fine demonstration of the heights of intelligence and the depths of dopery to which a dog can aspire. He is about five years old, and long ago he learned how to tell when his master and mistress were about to go out, leaving him alone in the house, a situation he detests. Whenever these clues come to him, he gets out into the large garden. And there, grinning maliciously away at the foot amid the bushes, he awaits developments. It used to take his master and mistress anything from ten to twenty minutes to catch him.

They discovered, however, a way to beat him at the game. Whenever he retreats to the foot of the garden, the master leaves the back door open, goes to the front door, opens it softly, rings the front door bell loud and long, and then re-opens and closes the front door loudly.

This proves too much for the cocker. Up he races from the garden and in the open door, to see who has come. The mistress is hiding behind the kitchen door, and slams it.

Trapped! The dope.

Nature the Equalizer

Nature, free of human interference, never looks for a bumper crop of anything in particular. She plays no favorites. All she is interested in is propagating life. Life in any form. The unseasonable frost that wipes out the blueberry crop for hundreds of square miles is wonderful for the germination of jackpine seeds. The low water that made the spawning of certain tribes of a fish for this season a complete failure is wonderful for the regeneration of plant life in the shallows. Gales that blow the drifting sand dunes to bury thousands of acres of plant life also lift up and carry millions of a hundred varieties of plant seeds hundreds of miles to fresh expectant soils. In nature, nothing comes amiss. The old bull moose lies down and dies. And forty guests come to the feast.

A spruce forest reaches its prime and can do no more. So its lowest branches become dry tinder, curled up to greet the lightning. The fire comes. The thick prime forest is destroyed. The ashes sink into the soil. The rampikes are blown down to make a tangle. The poplar arrives. It flourishes like weeds, and presently the beaver arrive to eat the poplar, and they dam the surface water that wanders over the riven land. Ponds grow. From distant parts, the seeds of spruce and pine and birch come on the gales. In the shelter of the poplars, in the moisture of the beaver ponds, they take root. In thirty years, the poplars are tottering. The spruce are rising. In eighty years, there will be another fine spruce forest, getting ready its tinder.

All nature is interested in is life. Any kind.

Rational

A twelve-year old nephew was standing with me at the windows of my upstairs den watching the five o'clock traffic grinding by. I live in an old part of the city on a street that used to be a quiet residential backwater, but which now, due to the thrombosis of traffic, has become a bypass for several main crosstown bottlenecks. Both morning and evening, our old houses tremble with the trample and crunch of thousands of cars and trucks, as the citizenry struggles to and from its labors.

The evening stampede begins shortly after four o'clock and by five has ceased to be a stampede. Traffic has been coralled. In all four directions which we can view from my den, there are motionless and rather frustrated looking lines of cars waiting their turn to cross an intersection and get onto a forty-mile-an-hour boulevard, half a block distant.

"Just look at the poor dopes," I exclaimed to the boy.

As far as we could see, not a car was moving in the doleful crawl home.

The boy was obviously puzzled by my irate yet condescending tone.

"Well," he said, "how else would they get home?"

We older folk make the mistake of supposing the young share our concern over the confusions of our time. No so. To them, it is the rational, normal way of life.

Top Deck Manners

You young people can have no idea of the manners your elders had to learn when they were young. It was most unladylike, and very ungentlemanly, to walk with your toes turned in. Especially most unladylike. And the more you turned your toes out, the more ladylike and the more gentlemanly you were. If you walked with your toes turned in, you were a lout. If you walked straight, you were plebian, common, ordinary. But if you toed out wide, you were likely to rise to be a bank manager.

Nor should we ever swing our arms as we walked. Only common workmen swung their arms. For a lady to swing her arms was considered utterly vulgar. You were supposed to walk politely, your arms hanging at your sides. This indicated that you had never carried a lunch pail, and it was most important to our generation that we should cover up the fact that our fathers or grandfathers had carried lunch pails. And picks and shovels too.

We were instructed severely in the arts of deportment, for our grandfathers were the sons and grandsons of immigrants, for the most part, who had toed in, swung their arms and ate everything on their plates.

What we were trying desperately to hide was the fact that we were the descendants of immigrants. We all wanted it understood that we had not come to Canada in

continued

the steerage, but on the top deck, up with the captain. If all we early Canadians had come across the Atlantic on the top decks, they must have been perilous voyages indeed, with the old sailing ships so top-heavy with the socially elite. Back in the eighteen hundreds, we all tried hard to marry into a family that had come out to Canada to some cushy job, such as the deputy-assistant-surveyor-general for the district of Canada West (a couple of counties) so that we could refer rather grandly to our ancestry, nine-tenths of which was good plain hod carriers and sod busters and pine sawyers. So about the time your grandfathers or great grandfathers were your age, Canada was full of old battle axes of spinster aunts, with whale bone holding up the lace collars around their long scrawny necks, whose function in Canadian society was to instruct us never to eat all that was on our plates, but always to leave a little daintily poked to one side with our forks. And always wear gloves. A young lady around 1900 who didn't wear gloves was likely to be a hussy. To this day, you will find old ladies who won't totter over to the post box on the corner without putting on their best hat and wearing gloves.

Don't toe in; never rest your elbows on anything, let alone the table; sit like a lady, to wit, heels together, back straight, and your mouth held pretty. Cross your hands, gloved, in your lap.

Never forget that one of your ancestors had enough pull, through his wife's first cousin's uncle, to get a clumsy job as secretary to the deputy-director of free seed potatoes to the loyalists in the colonies.

Bird Boxes: for Nesting or Decoration

Early fall, not spring, is the time for people interested in the sight or sound of small birds to put up nesting boxes. If they are put up in August or September they will have the winter in which to become weathered the way the birds like them.

And the birds you want to attract may come, the eye-blinding bluebird, the hotly-singing wren and various other characters who can add to the living beauty of your surroundings.

But birds have a way of peferring to do their own managing, thank you. Wrens are very glad of a box sometimes. But house sparrows and starlings are the only really eager customers. The only really successful man at attracting birds to his garden, among my acquaintances, lives in a suburban tangle of two acres. Not one bird house is visible. He makes his nesting boxes out of cedar or pine bark, and old weathered bits of wood. Some are the conventional boxes with entrance holes; others are mere shelves with tiny roofs over them. He uses flower pots, rusty tin cans and, for the owls, foot long lengths of drain pipe.

Every one of these nesting boxes is as invisible to the casual eye as are the nests the birds build themselves. You have to search for them in the bushes as you would for wild nests. That, of course, is the secret of his success in attracting the birds to live on his two acres.

Offering them shelter is only half his task. He scatters

continued

nesting materials seductively about the area, strips of shredded bark, waste wool from his wife's knitting bag, the odd handful of excelsior, little wisps of the crinkly paper used in packing china, and, from the barn of a farmer friend, strands of hair from horses' tails, festooned in the bushes. If the weather is dry during the nest-building weeks, he sets out pans of water around the premises, so that the birds can make their mud-pies for the nests, or soften up the materials.

A bird's nest is quite a bridey job.

Three-Bedroom Suburbs

On a February Sunday, I took a fine brisk walk up and down and across the streets on one of these new housing developments that have spread out far and wide around the perimeters of most Canadian cities and big towns. What I was looking for were grandmas and grandpas. And except for five elders who were obviously visiting for the afternoon, I saw not one.

It was a beautiful winter day. I saw any number of small children playing in the snow outside their pretty little homes. Quite a number of young parents were out walking or playing with their children. In the picture windows of the smart little bungalows, I caught glimpses of several people, men and women, but they were all young. Not one elderly woman stood watching out the window. No elderly man with the easy, proprietorial appearance of a resident of the neighborhood, did I meet pulling a grandchild's sleigh or strolling along for the air.

The only old people I saw had their hats and coats on, either arriving or just departing.

The question is: with this powerful trend towards smaller homes, with their two or three bedrooms, what becomes of the older generation?

If you are familiar with the older streets of a city, you know that the vast majority of the houses are two-generation homes; they have room, even in the old modest districts as well as in the more fashionable sections, for more than just a young married couple and their small children. You can prospect around a city and see streets built in the eighteen-eighties. Not very expensive homes, many of them semi-detached, but with six, seven, eight rooms. You can follow the growth of a city by its streets: the nineties, the early nineteen hundreds. Decade by decade, you can move forward into the twenties.

And then the bungalows began.

They have popped up, a hundred at a time, thousands in a year, in the new suburban subdivisions.

But there is no room in them for semi-detached grandparents. Grandmas and grandpas have been detached.

Antique

In an antique store window, I was shocked to see, along with early Victorian bronze urns, pioneer rocking chairs, Civil War sabres, blue china, butter tubs and other treasures—imagine! a Lee-Enfield rifle.

Yes, sir, there it was leaning in the corner with all the other relics of bygone days. I haven't had anything make me feel my age like the sight of this weapon in such company.

I studied it acutely. It was the good old Mark III, sure enough. Maybe because it was a little battered from noble use, it rated this public humiliation, in the opinion of the dealer, probably a woman!

But this was the weapon of the Old Contemptibles who, with rifle fire alone, halted the massive legions of the Kaiser at Mons. This was the sole arm, with its bayonet, which, by the millions, became in two years, the companion of the sons and friends of Britain who came from the four corners of the world to serve in that last of the wars of chivalry, 1914-18.

And it is antique!

They should have waited until we Mark III types are all gathered to our fathers.

The Survivor

At a recent dog show, after the sporting breeds had been judged, in which the hounds took part, the hounds were brought forth in their own group.

There were, in the final lineup, Irish wolfhounds, bloodhounds, Afghan hounds, Norwegian elkhounds, dachshunds of two varieties, the smooth and the long haired, a lonely foxhound and last of all and loneliest of all, a beagle.

They made a fine array. Here on show were all the strains of all the hunting companions of man from the ancient past. Strangest of all of course was the Afghan, with its silky hair combed in fantastic fashion in long strands off its high-domed narrow head, somewhat reminiscent of the poodle and also with a slight resemblance to an aging movie star who has spent too long at the beauty parlor.

The Irish wolfhound, as big as a yearling calf, won the prize. It was proper that it did, for this was a show of style, and since nobody has hunted wolves in Ireland since Brian Boru, nobody can know what an Irish wolfhound should look like except some fanciers who look upon dogs as livestock.

There in the parade were the caterpillaresque dachshunds toddling along, the bloodhound gloomy and clumsy, with not even an escaped female slave to chase, the elkhound who will never see an elk, the grotesque Afghan, and the foxhound whose days are numbered all

continued

over the world.

But last came the glorious, tidy little beagle, fourteen inches high at the shoulder, clean as a whistle, bland but wise of eye, tough as rawhide, pretty as a picture, tireless as the winds of heaven. He came last.

But all over America, he remains the one great multiplying, prospering hunter's hound, the only gentleman present in the hound show whose business is flourishing, and goes on day by day, the year round, regardless of shows.

It was faintly comic to see him in competition with pictures off memory's wall.

The Aspirate 'Erb

Nearly all Canadians pronounce herbs as 'erbs. This astonishes a newly arrived English lady. In Britain, she asserts, herbs is always pronounced with the aspirate H except among those English who just naturally leave the H off everything and put it where it isn't called for.

The English are about the only members of the British family who concern themselves to any extent with herbs. The Irish and the Scots are content with food as represented by the plainer victuals such as potatoes, stewed beef, oatmeal and haggis. But it stands to reason that it was the British settlers in Canada, rather than the Scots or Irish, who introduced herbs to this country. All you have to do is read Isaac Walton's description of how to dress a pike to see how dependent the English have been on herbs for centuries. The way Isaac stuffed a pike, all you could taste would be thyme, sweet marjoram and a little winter savory; some pickled oysters and a few anchovies; a blade or two of mace and the juice of three or four oranges; two cloves of garlic and all basted with claret wine. Yes: that is Isaac Walton's idea of a well-cooked pike.

Thus, meseemeth, it could have been the English who brought herbs to English-speaking Canada. And doubtless many of those English started calling herbs 'erbs. And so it stuck.

But we do not say erbivorous, nor do we say erbal, nor erbage, nor erbarium nor erbacious. No: we give them all H.

In some parts of the United States, and I have also encountered it in sections of Canada far back from the railroads, they pronounce herbs as yarbs.

I tried this on the English lady, and she agreed at once that yarbs is a much better word than 'erbs.

But herbs is better still.

Deer Killers

A trapper named Harold Roberts who is a northern outfitter in summer and runs a trapline in winter, was

continued

interested in the unusual amount of noise being made by a flock of ravens as he passed along his trapline. He snowshoed over to the scene of the ravens' excitement and found a dead fawn. It had recently been killed by predators, as it was in good condition and had certainly not died of starvation.

Roberts supposed it was wolves, and back-tracked in the snow, away from the beaten-up area where the fawn lay, to see if he could estimate the number and size of the marauders on his trapline. To his astonishment, he discovered nothing but fox tracks. Following the trail of the tragedy some distance, he was able to estimate that either five or seven foxes had formed a pack and had jumped the fawn in the snowdrifts and attacked it, dragging it down several times before finally overpowering it. No other animal appeared to be involved in the hunt.

A fox weighs from ten to fifteen pounds, as against the seventy to hundred and fifty pounds of a wolf. A fox terrier weighs eighteen pounds. A cocker spaniel weighs up to twenty-four pounds. A fox is a slender-boned, almost fragile animal compared to a dog. Seen in the fields or woods, its small size is exaggerated by its rich fur. Its jaws are small and snipey compared to a terrier's. To picture it attacking a deer required quite an effort of imagination, yet biologists inform me that families of foxes will form packs and have been known to do what Trapper Roberts definitely reports.

The significance of his report had to do with the chasing of deer by dogs. If a pack of five or seven foxes can destroy deer, what can packs of dogs left loose in the bush do—dogs three or four times the size of foxes and still not deemed to be in the class of wolves?

Smy

The news announcer on the radio said:

"It has been reported that an American smy has been arrested in Pinsk."

After a moment's reflection, he tried again.

"It is reported that an American spy has been arrested in Minsk."

That came out better. But still, personally, I like the word smy. It's a wonder the people who made up the English language didn't invent smy instead of spy.

Smy is far more descriptive. If you say it over and over a few times, you perceive that it is a sly, sneaky, furtive word. It connotes far better than the bright sharp word spy the impression most of us have in mind when we think of those baleful individuals who endanger us.

Yet such spies as I have seen were far from smies. On a wild winter night on the Arras front in the first world war, in the midst of a faked German raid on our trenches, a German feldwebel or sergeant-major surrendered to us. He was a British spy bringing news of an intended massive assault on the Somme. And a bigger, ruddier, heartier individual you could hardly imagine. On the liberation of the Fresnes prison in Paris in August, 1944, I met a number of our spies who had been captured by the Germans. And they were for the most part cheerful extroverts more like a bevy of commercial travellers than the smies of fiction.

Lost Scent

When I was courting forty years ago, I used to buy my sweetheart a corsage of violets and lily of the valley every Saturday night to wear to church on Sunday. And I tell you the perfume of it filled the church for pews and pews around.

For old time's sake not long ago I bought her another corsage of violets. And when I got home, we discovered there was not the slightest perfume to them. Yes, there was a slight odor, faintly musty, cellary, but not a trace of perfume.

"Maybe," I suggested bleakly, "we have lost our senses of smell."

But even the young people could detect no perfume. So I took the corsage back to the florist.

"You've left something out of these," I informed him.

He was very patient with me.

"Why, sir," he said, "you never saw more beautiful violets than those! See how big they are. Just look at the gorgeous color. And they are sturdy. They will last twice as long as the old fashioned violet."

"Mmm-hmmm," I encouraged.

"It is true, sir, that they no longer have the perfume of the violet of forty years ago. Certainly not. When you set out to improve a strain, and bend all your efforts to size, beauty, color, vigor, something is bound to be lost."

So I took the corsage out to the street and presented it

to an elderly newsboy who obviously had a bad cold in the nose and would never know the violets had no odor. He just thought I was daft.

And I walked the bright, tall streets amid the clangor and the rushing throngs and thought of all the savors, the perfumes, the tangibles, the fragiles and the loveliness that are lost in the name of size and color and vigor and I could think of a hundred of them.

And the more I counted, the lonelier I got.

Maximizer

"Keep your eyes open all the time," says a friend of mine, "and you'll get awfully sleepy."

As you can see, my friend is not much of a believer in some things we hold dear in these prosperous times.

"The early bird," he says, "looks kind of peaked, doesn't it? Maybe its the chill."

He has several about the grindstone. But the one he likes best about keeping your nose to the grindstone is just "Ouch!"

He took the full course in how to make friends and influence people.

"But," he says, "I took it in self defense. I just wanted to be alert to all the tricks smilers were likely to try to play on me."

"Look after the dollars," he reflects, "and the pennies

continued

will just have to look after themselves."

"A stitch in time," he finds, "is impossible, due to our new and improved methods of manufacturing. Throw the darn thing out and buy a new one."

"Heaven helps those," he has noticed, "who help themselves before passing the dish."

"A fool and his money," it occurs to him "have the most fun."

"If at first you don't succeed," he declares, "it is probably because you are just dumb."

From these maxims you might suppose my friend is a lazy, happy-go-lucky, humorously cynical character. On the contrary, he is a very straight laced, hard-working individual who for the past thirty years has devoted himself whole-heartedly to looking after his rich wife's business interests. We met as students at university and he announced to the whole world at the age of nineteen that his ambition, nay, his purpose in life was to be the very faithful husband of a very rich woman.

He managed it perfectly by being quietly charming.

"There's no place," he assures me, "like a nice big house."

1961

It will be in the year 6009 A.D. a long way from here before we get another year like 1961 in which you can turn the number upside down and get the same figures. Will there be any observers in 6009 A.D. dealing with trivialities such as this and reminding the public that the last time such a phenomenom occurred was back here, with us?

Will we appear as remote to them as to us do the Egyptians who, four thousand years ago, were busy with a great empire, building the pyramids that have survived to this day, erecting temples that outlasted those of Greece and Rome, exploring the heavens, though not outer space, and founding the sciences of astronomy, measurement and mathematics?

In 6009 A.D., our next counterpart in time, will anything much of our fabric, material or intellectual, remain?

What have we got that the Egyptians didn't have at Luxor? And what have we got that somebody will want in 6009 A.D.?

All that occurs to me on this the second day of 1961 is that the fishing won't be so good in 6009 A.D.

Square

Being a square, I have never yet heard a comprehensible definition of a square. At a recent family gathering of young people, I undertook enquiries, and it seems squares are all people over thirty, and about eighteen per cent of all people over eighteen.

I maintained that this was far too general a generality. The best definition I obtained from an elderly teen-ager in the group, aged twenty-four, with a beard. He said it was perfectly obvious.

,"A square," he said, "is someone who won't or can't fit into any other situation than with the other squares. A square is an uncomfortable shape. You can't arrange it except with other squares, see?"

I saw at once.

"Those who aren't squares, then," I realized, "are sort of soggy, and shapeless and kind of limp, eh? You can pack a hundred of them in a carton or an old fish box. They conform. They fit. They have no shape or form themselves, and can adapt themselves to . . . "

He suddenly realized I had said conform.

"No, no," he protested. "It's the squares that conform. They have to, to fit."

But I still think the most conforming thing in the world is a bagful of . . . er . . . mush?

Old Bogeys

The next thing to the bogey-man, when I was a child, was the policeman. Children were brought up in the fear of the Lord and the policeman. One of the functions of the police, cheerfully accepted by the cops themselves, long years before the phrase "public relations" was dreamed of, was to strike terror into the hearts of small evil-doers. Parents threatened naughty little boys with the awful fate of a policeman getting them.

And with stern and often forbidding mien, the cops lived up to their role. I recall a Plainclothesman Twigg, or Detective Twigg as he was called, because he went about without a uniform, who daily rode his bicycle slowly past our house both morning and afternoon, casting black, inscrutable glances to left and right as he moved almost majestically by. He would as soon have fallen ignominiously off his bike as smile. He was the law. And between Detective Twigg and the Rev. Mr. Mutch, an equally formidable gentleman who was to be seen almost every day walking solemnly along our street, we children had a very thorough and constant awareness of the consequences of evil-doing. Detective Twigg could put us in jail, and Rev. Mr. Mutch could consign us to hell. And of the two, I was more scared of jail.

A long, long way we have come in fifty years. My grandchildren today are taught that the policeman is their

continued

very best friend. And they can prove it. He helps them across the street. He smiles at them from a great height. He is fatherly, uncley. A boy was knocked off his bicycle in front of our house the other evening by a car. He was not hurt, but the motorist thought the police should be called. Just for the record. When the patrol car drew up, all the children in the neighborhood were waiting, and they swarmed around the police, offering all manner of advice and counsel, climbing into the squad car, pulling at the cops' sleeves and pant legs for attention, treating them almost as equals. The police were not harassed. They made their notes amid a din that did not disturb them and which they did not attempt to quell.

I thought with a shudder of Detective Twigg, and what he would have done in his day. Those of us who had not run indoors at his approach would be peering from side entrances.

And the Rev. Mr. Mutch? Ah, well, you can't tell a parson from a parent now. Even if they don't succeed, they all try to be buddies.

The Hawk

A lady neighbor of mine suffered a shocking experience the other day. A pair of robins had chosen the cornice of her back porch for a nesting site, a fine view of which could be had from the back bedroom upstairs. The nest building was proceeding in fine style and my neighbor was spending half hours at a time watching the job.

One of the robins was on the nest, busily turning round and round to mold the mud and grass into a cup, when there came a brief hissing sound, and a large silver grey hawk, probably a goshawk, struck like lightning out of the air, seized and instantly killed the robin with one clutch of its talons.

For a brief, savage instant, the hawk stood on the cornice, the robin in its grip. The horrified lady was staring out the window. The hawk saw her and favored her with a glare so fatal that it was hours before she could forget it. She came around to see me in the evening to get some words from me that would exercise the haunting memory from her mind. I couldn't give her any.

"The hawk," I said, "was not furious at you. He or she probably saw the look of horror on your face. And all he or she was doing was looking at you indignantly. It was saying to you: 'What, then, am I not to feed my young?'"

I had to give some such whimsical reply to her anguished queries. Because how can you explain to a gentle, sentimental lady that she herself belongs to a species far more savage and heartless than all the hawks in the world? How can you remind a kindly, soft-hearted lady that every day of her life depends on taking the life of some other living creature? Every day, a cow, a pig, a sheep must be emotionlessly slaughtered in order that she may have her bacon, her chops, her steak. A million hens must live in eternal and hopeless bondage in order that she may have her eggs, her omelettes, even her macaroons. How do we all come by this extraordinary notion that we alone, of all living creatures, have the divine right to kill and eat?

When she went home from my place, she was still weepy over that cruel, cruel hawk.

The Eulogy

I often wonder what clergymen talk about when they are by themselves. Often, in Pullman cars or in hotels when there are clerical gatherings, I have seen gentlemen of the cloth engaged in private converse, little groups of them, enjoying what must be jokes and even unseemly topics of private discourse, to judge by their laughter.

Well, I got hold of what may be one solution. They must talk about us mortals whom they so gravely serve. In a small town recently, there was a funeral of a local gentleman of great respectability, and everybody of any account attended. The clergyman was of the persuasion that feels called upon to declaim a eulogy over the dear departed.

Now, this dear departed had been a good man, and worthy, and properous. But he had spent a fairly colorless life, with little to afford a good bite on, for purposes of eulogy.

The parson mounted the pulpit in the funeral parlor and proceeded with the funeral service. Then he came to the place where the eulogy is spoken. There is always a special hush at this point.

His reverence launched quietly into a summary or brief biographical sketch of the departed, listing his many virtues. Finding his material a little commonplace, the parson searched about in his memory for bits and pieces of former funeral orations that had served well, and he warmed to his subject. In due course, he was dealing in superlatives, and he knew he had his audience properly spellbound.

Then he came to the end of his superlatives and could think of no more. Now for the dramatic close.

Leaning over the pulpit, he pointed down to the casket.

"My friends," he cried, "the shell is there. But the nut is gone!"

You could tell by the slow flush that welled up from his collar that the parson realized his words. You could tell by the tiny stirring among the mourners that many of them were having sudden trouble with their diaphragms.

But with a benediction, which bowed all heads, the service ended.

It is probably things like this that parsons talk about when they are by themselves.

Drama by a Quiet Lake

A towerman in the district of Gogama in northern Ontario was up in his eyrie watching, as towermen do, hour by hour, for the first telltale wisp of smoke from a forest fire when he saw, in a small lake not far from his tower, a cow moose come out to the shore and wade in amidst the lily pads. Behind her came two moose calves. The towerman picked up his field glasses for a close-up

continued

look at this pretty woodland entertainment.

The calves were very young, and characteristically ungainly on their long stilty legs. While the mother buried her head in the water to uproot the lily pads, the two calves gambolled about on the shore and took small experimental paddles on the water's edge.

The towerman was watching the calves when he saw, in the edge of the field of his binoculars, a bear suddenly come crouching out of the underbrush back of the shore. It took cover behind some sedges and waited until the cow moose, munching on lily pads, again buried her head in the water to uproot a fresh supply. And then the bear charged.

It seized one of the paralyzed calves by the neck, and, hoisting it, retreated to the bush, part of the time on his hind legs, part of the time dropping to all fours to drag; and before the cow moose raised its head, the bear and the calf vanished into the brush. The cow, puzzled, stared around, and then came ashore, to run in bewildered circles around the remaining calf, and sniffing frantically at the bear scent in the air.

It was a drama in one act, consuming less than half a minute of time.

After a few moments of frenzied circling, the cow led the surviving calf off down the shore and into the bush.

The towerman is one of those who, next spring, when the suckers are running by the thousands in all the creeks, will dip himself a few hundred to toss out on the shore to rot and stink. But a few dozen he will take to nearby pens, made of old logs and stumps, and there he will shove them into the pen. And in the entrance to the pen, he will set a great, grim bear trap, with iron chains affixing it to drag logs.

And when he gets a bear, he will think of that moose calf, and skin the bear and sell the hide to a tourist.

Tartans

A Mr. McMahon of my acquaintance deals in dress goods and was showing me some of the newly arrived ancient tartans from Scotland. These are most beautiful fabrics, far lovelier to my eye than the gaudy tartans that came into fashion about a century ago when Queen Victoria chose Balmoral as her country home and the Scottish clans and the textile industry rose in splendor to the possibilities of the occasion and produced clan, dress and hunting patterns that, in their color, must have been a great relief to the endless drabness of the long-tailed coats, grey ties, black hats of that era.

These ancient tartans are muted, soft, lovely. They are in tones one associates with the heather hills of that glorious lone land.

On the shelves behind Mr. McMahon, as he showed me the ancients, were the giddy bolts of the conventional tartans. I should tell you, now, that Mr. McMahon is an Irishman.

"I had a lady," he said, "of very Scottish tongue and disposition in here the other day, and she went into ecstasies over the display of tartans here on the shelf. She exclaimed. She said she could name every one of them. And she proceeded to name them, all fifteen of them you can see. She had them all wrong but two."

"Did you enlighten her?" I enquired.

"My gosh!" said Mr. McMahan, "you don't enlighten the Scotch!"

Elevated

A Canadian who has spent most of his life in Britain and acquired some distinction there has a great gift of rubbing people the wrong way. I have met the gentleman several times both at home and abroad, but I appear to be the sort of person who does not register with him, since he makes it perfectly obvious that he has not met me before. And when he asks me what I do for a living, and I tell him my business, he exclaims with warm interest:

"Ah, I know your employer very well, very well indeed."

Out of a gang of newspapermen to whom I told this anecdote, two immediately declared that the gent had pulled the same remark on them.

"It is part of his stock-in-trade," one of them explained. "If you had talked for any length of time to him he would have lightly referred to some eminent peer by his last name, leaving the title off, which is the acme of cozy familiarity, and would have assured you, out of his affection for your employer, that he would be glad to help you in any way, among the big brass, in case you needed assistance."

A great man once said no man added to his stature by standing on his dignity. Some men manage nicely to elevate themselves in their own esteem with such simple gimmicks as this.

Isaiah's Warning

There is a text in the Bible that I have never heard preached upon in sixty years, and it seems to me that it should have been one of the important texts of that very period. It is Isaiah 5: 8, and it was C.R. Tilt who brought it to public attention in an article in the Canadian Geographical Journal on our provincial parks.

"Woe unto them that join house to house, that lay field to field, till there be no place that they may be placed alone in the midst of the earth."

Until about a hundred years ago, cities and towns were depots, collections of warehouses, shops and factories whose function was to serve the bulk of mankind who lived on the land. But in the present century, the movement of population into cities, towns and villages has, in the most peopled areas of Canada, reduced the proportion of those on the land to something like a third of the total. House has been joined to house by the hundreds of thousands. Thanks to mechanization, the declining numbers on the land have been able to join field to field so that there is literally no place where anyone may be alone in the midst of the earth. As a child, I went on picnics half a mile from the city limits. We took the streetcar to the end of the line, walked half a mile on country roads, and in no time had found a piece of woodland that apparently belonged to nobody, and there picnicked undisturbed, alone in the midst of the earth.

How far do we have to go now to be alone in the midst of the earth? Woe unto us, we are expected to picnic in a public picnic ground allocated by the government and full of company.

Creatures of Night

Being members of the mammal family ourselves, and addicted to daylight saving, it comes as a surprise to us to learn that by far the greater number of our fellow mammals are nocturnal and live their entire lives asleep by day and active by night. A naturalist of the University of Michigan points out that squirrels, chipmunks, groundhogs and prairie dogs, like deer, moose, sheep, goats and bison are daylight animals. To some extent, cats, foxes, coyotes, hares and rabbits, though chiefly active by night, are fairly commonly seen by day. But against these few he sets up the enormous company of the mice, moles, rats, shrews, bats not to mention the raccoon and numerous other larger animals that wake up at dusk and engage furiously in their livelihood almost exclusively in the dark.

Every hunter knows that dawn and dusk are the likeliest times of day to see the deer, which rest most of the full daylight hours and feed in the half-light of early morning and evening. If they sleep at night, it must be a restless business, knowing that the wolf, the lynx and to some extent the bear are on the prowl when so many of their small prey, the hares and mice and other rodents are up and about and easily detected. We share with birds the sense of night as a time of peace and quiet and rest. But to perhaps the great majority of living things, including the insects, reptiles, fish and an immense population of animals, the night is life itself. Their world is not our world at all. They have different vision, sharper sense of hearing and smell. Night has terrors for us. Day has the same terrors for them.

No better time of year can be chosen than August to choose a listening place, on a cottage veranda or in a car parked in a wood to verify this immense activity of the living night. As I write this, I have just heard, across a mile of rock and muskeg, the rabble sound of a mother wolf and her pups who have just jumped a deer and given brief and vain chase. By the time the snow comes, and the pups are grown, the chase will not be so brief, nor perhaps so vain.

Verbal Vandals

In a little biographical sketch of one of our outstanding public figures was the fact that he and his wife close their day by reading aloud to each other. Sometimes it is a detective thriller. Or it might be one of the good books of the year, noticed by all the reviewers. Occasionally, it said, they read the newspaper aloud.

A more horrible picture of connubial bliss would be hard to conjure up. Imagine the two of them, middle-aged, propped up in bed, spectacles on their noses, eloquently reading aloud. How long do they read? Half an hour? An hour? Does the read-ee start to snore? Is that the signal for lights out? Or does the party of the first part

continued

go right on droning to the end of the chapter. It is thoughts like this that disturb my own rest.

If this appears to some to be overreaction to an account of innocent and homely domesticity, I confess I hate reading aloud on anybody's part, anywhere, any time. I have a relative who brings all the letters she gets from her nephews, nieces, and even friends who are on a motor trip, and sits in my living room, and in a loud, ringing voice, with all suitable elocutionary effects, including gestures, eyebrows, punctuation marks and exclamation points, reads the blame things from page one to page eight. Another of my burdens is a male who seizes the paper the minute it arrives and reads aloud all the exciting items, the weather, the jokes on the editorial page, with suitable comments on each.

By the time I get hold of the paper, it is second-hand. It's used. Reading aloud should be confined to the pulpit, the mortuary parlor and the court of law.

The Squelcher

There are a great many people who profess to love music who are sheer frauds. A person who loves music is incapable of conversation while good music floods from the radio or phonograph. The frauds are those who chatter, murmur or blather in the midst, say, of a Brahms concerto.

In England I encountered an Englishman who loved music, and we went to the Albert Hall together to hear the famed Solomon at the piano in concert with one of the great London orchestras. My friend was a large, tweedy, shaggy-mustached man with a ruddy face. You would not take him for a Bach lover. He lived in the country and came down to London for concerts.

During the opening number, two frizzy women in evening dress with spectacles on their high thin noses continued to chatter quietly. They were seated immediately behind us. My large friend turned several times and glowered. So did others in the vicinity. Then Solomon came on and received an ovation as he sat to the piano. After about ten bars, the two women began quietly chattering as before.

My friend squirmed and wriggled as he got his raincoat from under him. From the pocket, he removed a London newspaper, the Daily Telegraph, a fairly bulky paper by wartime London standards. He rolled it up neatly. Then, suddenly he turned in his seat and dealt the noisiest frizzy lady a wallop right on the top of the head.

Not a hard blow, but just a good slap such as you would give a naughty pup. There was, of course, a startled snicker all around. But certainly no more chatter. After the concert, when I asked the Englishman why on earth he had done such a thing, he said:

"If I had remonstrated with them, they would have stood upon their rights. This is England, you know: a free country. But when you bat them over the head like that, they always shut up. You've got to know how to handle them."

The Price of Mink

A lady wearing a mink coat told me it had cost $4,000.

How she came to inform me of this fact arose as follows: we were sitting in a doctor's waiting room; she awaiting the arrival of her husband to take her home; I for my turn to show the doctor my tonsils. Her cigarette fell out of its gold and ivory holder. She thought it had fallen into the folds of her beautiful coat and leaped up in squealing agitation. I found the butt on the floor, and she directed me to drop it in the ash tray. When I sympathized with her distress, she informed me the coat had cost all that money, $4,000. . . .

In the ensuing silence, for she was a lady who preferred her own thoughts to continuing conversation with butt-rescuers, I admired the coat, but thought how long and how hard some of my acquaintances—chief clerks, self-employed service people—would have to work to buy one like it. Months—years—of scrimping, saving, doing without lunches, smokes, movies, new clothes, holidays. But ah, in the end, he would be able to buy his wife a beautiful incredible coat like this.

In a doctor's waiting room, you have such imaginings.

How wonderfully, I thought, a woman must love and cherish a man who would so work to give her a $4,000 coat!

The waiting room door opened. It was the husband.

"Where the hell," demanded the lady, "have you been!"

Swallows

One of the nesting boxes in view of our cottage veranda has been occupied several years by tree swallows. These beautiful swift birds, steel blue on the back and white on the breast cut their arabesques in silence all spring and summer in the air around the cottage.

It is a pleasure to watch the parent birds showing the wide world to the young, when they are out of the box. Professional ornithologists will doubtless have some scientific explanation of the behavior of the birds as they play about the neighborhood, returning time after time, seconds apart, to the nesting box, almost alighting, then swerving away, to waft like aimless arrows through the air. Is it the parents teaching the young that the nest is now no longer their home? That their home is now the whole wide sky, clear down to the Carolinas and the Gulf of Mexico, where they will winter?

I think it is sheer play, rejoicing in the feeling of life. What is the meaning of life to these tree swallows, steel blue and white? Can it be the joy of being alive? That is a good meaning.

The Touch

A renowned surgeon was attending a symphony concert. In his hip pocket he had his wallet containing a tidy sum of cash and a fistful of credit cards.

When the symphony was over, he with his wife wended their way out of the concert hall in the dense throng that slowly edges its way to the exits and the hat check room.

As they shuffled along, amid the happy, relaxed and loud murmuring crowd, the surgeon felt something touching him from behind. It was, he thought to himself, some elderly person, someone with one of the forms of palsy, for the touch on his posterior happened more than once.

If it had been you or I, no matter how bemused and relaxed and out of this world we might have been as a consequence of the beautiful music we had been hearing, we would have leaped instantly to the conclusion that somebody was after our precious wallet.

He found himself speculating mildly as to which of the forms of palsy the person behind him was afflicted with. He wondered what age he might be, or might it be a woman? He was, of course, much too polite to turn and look.

The palsied one ceased pushing from behind. The surgeon followed the throng and took his place in the line at the hat check room. He had put his hat check in his wallet. He reached for it. It was gone.

I like several things about this story. First, I suppose, is the thought that pickpockets too may love fine music. Why not, indeed? But most I like the idea of the distinguished man, unique among us for his gifts of mind and hand, being ever the healer, and mistaking the touch of the criminal for the symptom of something to be healed.

Devout

An elderly parson friend whom I met in a second-hand book store where he was looking for God knows what and I was exploring the section devoted to angling, told me that he had been retired three years and now occupied himself with occasional pulpit assignments and visits to country parishes.

"And funerals," he added. "It is surprising how many funerals we old-timers are dug out for."

"Hang on," I assured him, "and you can have mine."

"When you are a young man," he reflected, there among the lovely old worn books, "you put them all to their rest with a high heart. But as you grow older, and when you become as old as I am, you wonder if hell is as obsolete as has been constantly supposed for the past fifty years."

"Padre!" I protested.

"No," he said. "Only yesterday, I had to officiate at the funeral of a well-to-do elderly woman whose pastor I had been in bygone years. She was a masterful woman, if you can employ such a phrase. She was an indefatigable church worker. She gave most generously to all church funds and causes. When I was younger, I supposed she was a most

continued

ardent and devout Christian. But before I was through with her, and her family, I realized that she used her Christian virtues as a front to defend her own selfrighteousness. What she willed was right. How could she be wrong, if she were a pious church-going, upright Christian? And this attitude applied not only to her poor family, but to the grocer, the milkman, the clerks in stores, and her unhappy maids. She ruled with an iron hand, because she was a demonstrably good woman."

"Padre!" I pleaded.

"I had the queerest feeling," he said, and I noticed the two books he had picked up were Kipling's *Kim* and Casc's *Concise French Dictionary*, "that as I spoke the final benisons over her, God would meet her with a pail and a mop, and say to her 'Woman, get busy!' "

"Padre!" I objected.

"Pride," he said, "is the sin against the Holy Ghost."

What I bought was Izaac Walton's *Compleat Angler*, a very mussed up copy that somebody must have read with repeated devotion.

Stamp Out Porcupines . . .

Porcupines have more ways of inflicting pain than with their quills. I imagine no dog with a face full of quills feels any more pain than my neighbor up at the cottage resort who has just had his pet tree girdled and killed by a fat porky.

This neighbor has always reproved the rest of us who kill porcupines when we find them in the vicinity of our cottages. He thinks porcupines are quaint and comic and full of an absurd dignity. He keeps telling the rest of us that the porky today is identical with the porcupine found in fossil remains a million years old. The porky has not had to change, to readapt itself to changing aeons of time, as nearly all other species of animals have had to do. It was adequate from the start.

A couple of porcupines took up residence under our neighbor's cottage. Apart from chewing a few cartons to get the glue off them, and gnawing a joist here and there and trying to chew their way into the ice house, they did no harm, he assured us.

Then a handsome pine tree that was part and parcel of the landscape of his cottage mysteriously began to sicken. Its topmost and most bannerlike branches died. In the autumn, he observed that a white oak tree that gave character to his whole location appeared to have had all its upper twigs dropped off.

Next spring, when he arrived at the cottage to take off the shutters he was horrified to find that a slender young soft maple that had grown up by the side door of the cabin, a silvery, beautiful tree, had been girdled and was as dead as a stick.

Sadly he sent for the son of the local caretaker of the resort and told him to get his .22 rifle and dispose of the porcupines as humanely as possible.

The boy went around the point and did quite a bit of shooting.

"Did you get them both?" asked the cottager, sadly.

"I got seven," replied the boy.

. . . Or Try Red Pepper

A jar or tin of red pepper, not paprika, but the real hot cayenne, is a useful thing to take to a summer cottage or camp to offend porcupines and other nocturnal visitors that you do not wish to deal with more sternly. Many a cottager who hasn't the heart to shoot a porky has to submit to having canoes, boats and paddles chewed, toilet seats defaced and a variety of other damages inflicted on his premises. Being very habit-formed, a porky will almost invariably return to a job of chewing he has undertaken. So a little sprinkle of cayenne on the object of his attention and on any other handy items that might attract his notice will send the stupid creature off in a hurry, and he is not likely to return. Veterinarians assure me the pepper does him no harm, but merely adds to his collection of interesting olfactory experiences. It gives his nose, for a moment, a little taste of the business he gives a dog.

Last year, I planted a number of seedling jackpines in sandy pockets around my cottage. A family of raccoons share the point with me and are in the habit of coming around about midnight to see what the Clarks had for supper. They rattle the garbage pail, try all the screen doors, make off with any parcels that might have inadvertently been left outdoors. And when they found freshly disturbed earth around each of the baby jackpines, they naturally suspected a turtle must have been laying eggs there. So they uprooted each and every pine, finding nothing but mystery. Why, asks a coon, should anybody dig in the earth if not to bury something? Several of my seedlings died, despite repeated and most tender planting, before red pepper was suggested by an old settler among the neighbors. The effect was prompt. For good measure, and with not a little malice, I sprinkled some cayenne on the lid of the garbage pail, and around the other favorite night spots of the coons.

The raccoons moved right off the point, and are now taking up with some neighbors across the bay.

Here Comes Old Blank

All you young people under sixty should be kind and compassionate enough to carry one of those little name tags you see people wearing at conventions. It is a little clear plastic square, with a safety pin to fasten it to your lapel. And framed in it, a bit of paper, with your name, printed large.

And whenever you approached some old friend who is over sixty, you would whip out this name tag and hastily pin it to your coat. After sixty, you are in the habit of forgetting your nieces' and nephews' names. You meet somebody you have worked at the next desk to for forty years. And blooie! Blank.

Especially if you are with your wife. At the theatre just

continued

lately my old friend Samuel Hersenhoren, the orchestra conductor, came to me. My wife was sitting beside me. Now, who in the world could forget a name like Hersenhoren? You might as easily forget Auchterloney or Przmsl. Besides Samuel wears a small crew-cut beard. Yet, do you think I could remember Hersenhoren? I was going to introduce him to my wife as Giacomo Puccini, but he went away.

A moment later, the mayor of my city, Mayor Phillips, and his wife kindly greeted us. But one disaster, in this business of name-losing, breeds another. I introduced Mayor Phillips as Mayor McBride, who has been dead and gone these thirty years.

One of my nieces bent over us.

"Uncle Greg, Aunt Helen!" she cried, petting us.

"Darling," I responded, guardedly.

The Shovel

A few of my relatives are farmers still, though most of the tribe have slipped away into city and town to live by their wits. One of the farmer cousins was visiting the house when a late-winter snow storm blanketed the city. The dishes were done, the TV was on, but I had to go out with the snow shovel and clear the front walk.

The farmer offered to come and do it, even in his city clothes. But we have only the one shovel. So he put his hat on and came and stood on the front step to keep me company.

"Hey, just a minute!" he protested, as I started the snow flying. "What's the hurry?"

I rested on my shovel.

"Well, I want to get the job done," I suggested.

"Now, look," said my cousin, "a job is a job. That isn't the way to shovel snow. My gosh, man, you'll wear yourself out. Here, give me that shovel. . . . "

I declined, and bent to the task again, taking it a little more deliberately.

"The trouble with you city people," he reflected, muffler on neck, hands in pockets, "is that you don't understand a job is a job. It deserves to be done. But it deserves more than that. It deserves a little dignity. It shouldn't be treated as if it was hateful, as if there was no pleasure in it."

"You mean," I rested, again, "that shovelling snow should be a pleasure?"

"Well," said my cousin, puzzled, "there ought to be pleasure in all jobs. If there isn't, can you imagine how much work would be done in this world? I'm thinking, of course, of forking out the stable, or milking the cows on a cold night. But in the city, there must be no end of jobs that, if you didn't take some pleasure out of them. . . . "

I went slower. I saved my wind and muscles. I shoved the shovel, lifted the snow, emptied the shovel easily. I figured there was no hurry. It was pleasant on the snowy night. I had a long way to go, down the walk, along the front. What was the hurry? The snow falls. It has got to be removed. A job is a job. My cousin came down to take the shovel. I refused. He stood talking about how you go at each job, pleasantly, sparing yourself, taking it easy, finding pleasure in doing it, and in feeling it done.

The best snow job I've done in years.

Good Guys Have to be Sneaky

The late Jimmie Frise, the cartoonist, and I, who shared an office studio, were once beset by a plague of panhandlers and bums who found us easy marks for a hand-out. You cannot pretend to be simple and good-hearted fellows on paper and at the same time to be flint-hearted in private. But it began to hurt. We were both broke by 5 p.m. daily.

So we took counsel with ourselves and decided that we would help only the unworthy cases. Each character, when he came in for the touch, we asked: "Well, now, are you a worthy case?"

And when the victim hastened to assure us that he was indeed a worthy case, we promptly informed him that there were all sorts of agencies in town for looking after worthy cases. There was the Community Chest, and the numerous social service organizations, the welfare bureau at City Hall, the churches, the Salvation Army and all the rest of them dedicated to the worthy cases.

"We only help unworthy cases," we explained, gravely, "for those for whom there is no provision."

For a time it worked. Few men, however derelict, can bring themselves to confessing themselves unworthy. Jimmie and I, for a time, got home after work with as much as a couple of bucks in our pockets.

But presently the panhandlers and bums worked it out.

After due reflection, they decided they were no longer worthy cases. And the siege commenced all over again, on a much lower plane. To prove how unworthy they were, they would come in fighting drunk. So in the end, we resorted to a sign on our locked office door which read: "Out. Will be back in three hours." Then we told the worthy to ignore the sign, rap three times, pause, and then rap once.

Put in a Word for Nature

Probably because of the humility it inspires in us, Easter is in some respects a more tender season for the Christian than Christmas. This may be the reason that one of my fellow amateurs of nature who happens to be a clergyman has suggested that among our Easter prayers we remember to include one for the myriad creatures who share with us the miracle of life and resurrection.

"Pray," he said, "for the millions of birds, fragile, beautiful atoms, that are right this week homeward bound across thousands of miles of peril, from Brazil, Colombia, Yucatan, that they may sing and nest among us in another three weeks. Pray that they get a fair passage and safe home. Pray for the deer that are now in their last weeks

continued

of pregnancy, and all the rivers swollen and the treachery of April surrounding them. For the fox, the mouse, the squirrel. They are all expecting. Their time is upon them."

My friend got wound up.

"Pray," he said, "for the flowers that are stirring under the earth, putting up their frail shoots, that no frost catches them. And for the insects, by the billion, the butterflies, the dutiful beetles, each with its task, that are right now in the moment of resurrection."

A man can think of a lot of things to pray for at Easter.

The Better System

My father in his declining years, was my passenger one day as I drove him to his summer cottage from the city. He was a delightful passenger. He was one of those people who must comment on everything seen in passing. For example, when we went by a prosperous farm house which was notable because of the extraordinarily big and beautiful stacked woodpile, my father remarked with lively interest guessing at the identity of the farmer, supposing him to be an industrious immigrant with a large ambitious family.

As we journeyed along, an American motor car passed us going our way, and its spare tire on the rear revealed an election sign painted around the tire cover. "Elect

Schwartz Judge Erie County."

My father sat up eagerly as one suddenly called upon to make a speech.

"Ah, my boy," he declared, "there is the American tragedy! the elected judiciary. Who is this man who is offered as a candidate for the office of judge? Some shyster lawyer. Some ward heeler who is in the cahoots if not the pay of one of the political parties! Some political boss has said to this Schwartz, 'we will elect you judge, providing you dispense favors from the bench to the party.'

"How different," enunciated the old gentleman, swelling, "is our British system, whereby we appoint our judiciary for life; and only the life-long friends of the judiciary can expect any favors!"

Professional

A burglar paid a visit to our house while it was shut up for the vacation. Police came and investigated, when neighbors reported the back dining room window open. They report that the burglar was an expert, a professional. The way he cut the window glass, the way he snitched over the window latch and faultlessly pried the window up, leaving not a scratch on the painted sill, shows that he was a skilled mechanic in his trade.

Some of our friends who have been burgled complain of the muss and wreckage left by the intruders; drawers

continued

dumped on beds, clothing flung all over the place. Our burglar was the soul of tidiness. He was deft. One might almost suspect it was a woman burglar, and a good housekeeper at that.

Jewel boxes and trinket cases were left open and rifled on the top of dressers. Desk and secretary drawers and pigeon holes had been disturbed, but only enough to make sure that no bonds or other negotiable valuables were concealed there. He was not interested in table silver, even. Just rings, brooches, watches, and only standard watches at that. Any odd or curious watches he left severely alone. He got a few hundred dollars worth of things that can be replaced at any shop any place. I think he was a dull mechanical sort of expert. He must have been sadly disappointed in the contrast between the outside and the inside of my house. He could not know that the only real wealth in my house was a collection of old American and Canadian angling and hunting books, worth a great deal to the antique book trade, but impossible to dispose of as stolen loot, because the whole antique book trade would know they were mine. A few antique weapons that won't shoot, ten jars of wild strawberry jam, some pictures of my children and my forebears, a couple of old tweed jackets—that's all I treasure, and the dumb mechanic of a burglar didn't want them. You can detect from this that his disdain for my treasures left me grumpily offended.

The police left an awful mess. They daubed the whole house with white or black fingerprint powder and then walked out. The police should carry a housekeeper with them.

Gamut

When you are twenty, you have no patience with elderly men. They are obviously suffering from hardening of the arteries. But you have to be respectful to them. They can be dangerous. They are your bosses.

When you are thirty, you have a kindly, almost a quizzical attitude towards elderly men. You know in your heart that in a little while you will have ousted them. They can't last much longer.

When you are forty, you are shocked every now and then to note that some school chum you meet on the street has a pot belly, has gone bald and grey at the temples. You look about you. There are not so many elderly men as there used to be. . . .

When you are fifty, there comes a day as sure as fate when you encounter somebody who was a boy in short pants the last time you saw him. And something terrible has happened to him. He is still a boy, but his hair is already greying, his features have hardened so that you can barely recognize the boy in him. He is forty.

When you are sixty, you have no patience with young men. They are obviously suffering from softening of the brain. But you have to be respectful to them. For you know in your heart that in only a little while they will be ousting you.

In the case of a woman, it is entirely different. When

continued

a girl is twenty, she has no patience with elderly women, because obviously they are suffering from hardening of the arteries. But they do not have to treat the elders with any respect, because there is nothing on earth the elderly women can do about it.

When a woman is thirty, she thinks she is forty and tries to be twenty. By the time she is forty, she has no use whatever for girls of twenty, for obviously they are suffering from softening of the brain.

When she is fifty, she might as well be sixty, for from there in, her heart and soul is all for the twenty-year-olds, whom she wishes she could rescue from being over thirty.

The Supernatural Smudge

Cigarette smokers are divided into two categories; those who tamp their cigarette butts out with purpose and precision; and those who give their butt a slither-fiddle in the ash tray and leave them to smoulder and stink.

Character can be read in cigarette butts as readily as in any other behavior. I know a bank manager who always gives a cigarette to the strange customer asking for a loan; and he reserves his decision until he sees how the customer disposes of the butt.

Gordon Sinclair, the writer and radio commentator, has travelled round and round the world exploring all the byways off the main highways. He has seen queer things, eaten strange food, slept in curious places. But nothing irks him as much as smouldering cigarette butts. It is his greatest irk.

He claims that the smoke from a smouldering butt in an ash tray will invariably drift to him, rather than to anybody else in the same room. He goes further than that: he says that the smoke will follow him around if he changes his place. In a radio studio one day where you are commanded, of course, not to smoke by large signs on the wall, but where everybody smokes anyway, Gordon demonstrated this mysterious fact to me. One of us had left a butt burning and Gordon uttered his customary malediction on the offender. He told us how the smoke would follow him. We challenged him. He moved to the far end of the table. The smoke from the butt quickly shifted its course and went to him. He moved to the opposite end. The smoke gently reversed and wafted his way. We were transfixed. "Maybe," we suggested, "you are smoke-genic or something . . . " But Gordon merely said that the more a thing irks you, the more it will pester you. It's psychic, he said.

Remembrance

How little war really means to us is best demonstrated in the fact that we set aside one minute of silence out of the 525,600 minutes of the year as a mark of respect and mourning for the 58,000 Canadians killed in action in the first war, and the 39,000 in the second war. We declare a whole day for remembrance. But we gravely suggest one minute for silence; and hardly anybody remembers.

Thus lightly is war brushed off by all save the true mourners. And even some of them forget.

A woman of my acquaintance lost her husband in the first war and her son in the second. She was invited to attend ceremonies on each of three days, on November 11 and on the succeeding Saturday and Sunday, one by her husband's regiment, one by her church and one by her son's school.

I offered to be her escort.

"As a matter of fact," she said, declining, "every day is Remembrance Day with me. Every day, every night, all the year through."

War, you see, except for a little time while it rages, is not a public matter at all. In the long view, it is almost entirely a private matter.

Fulmar

Every day of a six-day trans-Atlantic steamer voyage, those inexhaustible birds, the fulmars, were seen about the ship. It was October. We were taking the northern route, to come down through the Straits of Belle Isle. Yet these beautiful gull-like birds were to be seen all over the ocean, both near the ship and as far as one could see with binoculars.

Except for a few weeks ashore in spring, to nest, the fulmars spend their entire lives far out over the ocean. It is their pasture, their home. They rest on the sea, I suppose. But in the six-day voyage, I never saw one alight on the water. They are a petrel, a little smaller than a common gull. They have snow white heads and breasts, and grey wings and backs. Their wings are shorter and more fin-like than a gull's, and are used almost entirely for soaring, skating, gliding through the air, just clear of the waves. Now and again, they give a few quick beats of these stiff little wings; but most of the time you watch them, they are gliding, with, across and fair into the wind.

Most ocean passengers suppose them to be gulls, following the ship. A few do follow the ship for a while, to see what the ship churns up. But for a dozen of them around the ship, there are a hundred visible far off, eternally sailing low over the ocean pastures, from which they pick up the small marine biological organisms on which the fulmars feed, and with which the surface of the sea abounds.

We think of the sea as a homeless place; but it is not so. It is home to countless thousands of fulmars and many

continued

other kinds of smaller petrels, not to mention other species that scorn the land, all their lives, except as a place on which to lay an egg.

Distraction

A lady complained to me that she would have to get her eyes examined.

"In church," she said, "I can no longer see the choir."

"Do you want to see them?" I asked before I could recollect my manners. For there are a great many people in the world who honestly do like to watch a church choir making those faces. On the other hand, there are a great many people like myself whose church-going life has been more or less wrecked by the choir. When I was very small I was always taken to a Presbyterian church which had a choir that was utterly comic. When I think of them now, I get a pain in the stomach. There was not an un-comic face in the whole outfit. The tenor was a fat man with a large up-tilted grey beard. The bass turned side-ways when he sang, in an attempt, never quite successful, to conceal the fact that to get his low notes, he had to sing out of the side of his mouth, from under a drooping mustache that waggled. The sopranos were lean, gape-mouthed, awful. The contralto, who did solos, quivered like custard and jelly every time she reached for a note. As a child, I got spanked for snorting and giggling in church, and have never forgotten it. A choir, even now, always gives me that pain in the jaws you get from trying to keep a straight face.

In the Anglican church, I found the choir stands sideways to you, and all you see, as a rule, is the end man or lady. That is not too bad. In the Catholic church, I was delighted to discover that the cathedral choir is in a gallery, unseen unless you are irreverent enough to crane around. Being a newspaperman, I have never been free to confine my worship to one church. Some of us are in duty bound to share the worship of all our fellow-citizens, and some strange things I have seen. But choirs always give me a pain somewhere, in my jaws, my stomach, somewhere. Personally, I love singing. But I hate to see it being done. It is time those who sing should know that some of us just can't bear the sight of it. As kids, we got off on the wrong foot.

Snake-Bitten

A common water snake about two feet long and the thickness of a cigar wriggled across the water between Levi Simon's boat and mine where we were tied to a wharf.

"Want to live to be a hundred and five?" called Levi.

"Sure."

"Then let that snake take a bite of you," said Levi, who is Ojibway. "On the leg or the arm. Pick him up and let

continued

him give you a good bite. You'll then live to a hundred and five."

Levi, who is an elderly man now, is the son of Henry Simon, who fifty years ago used to spin Indian tales and legends for us children gathered around the campfire. Levi, who is our best oar and paddle maker on the great Georgian Bay still, who can make an eight-foot oar in nine minutes from the blank wood to the beautiful finished blade, spoon and all, has preserved much of the ancient lore of his fathers back into the untouched forest. I told him that the common water snake was as harmless as a mouse or any other small creature that would bite in self-defense. But Levi replied:

"Even so. If you want to live to be a hundred and five. It has often been proved."

This recalled to mind what the late George Hebson Corsan once told me. Corsan, who was a great swimmer and teacher of swimming and life saving and who installed some of the finest wild life sanctuaries for wealthy Americans like the Kellogg estate, lived to a great age. Indeed, in his eighties, he fell out of a nut tree and broke his neck but lived another span of years. When a young man, he was bitten by a copperhead in Kentucky, and hung between life and death for two months. But he recovered and proceeded to live his vigorous and colorful life of close to nine decades.

"I owe my health and vigor," he told me, "to that snake bite. It did something to me. It roused some deep inner life force in me that has remained all my live."

Could it be that there is something psychosomatic in a snake bite, rousing to unsuspected powers and capacities the mysterious glandular complexities and interrelations which are still a mystery to science? Far back in the remote history of man, there must have existed an overpowering fear of serpents. What authority might that fear not have, now, on long forgotten functions of the human system?

Missing Verse

All of us who were born before 1900 learned to sing "God Save the Queen" under the great imperial monarch Victoria. Every one of us, with a certain unction, has counted back to discover that he or she has lived under six monarchs. It gives us a certain inner pomp.

When I first learned "God Save the Queen," it had three verses. Now on searching through hymn books and other poetical sources, I can find only two. Some years ago at a service of intercession in St. Paul's Cathedral, the bob-tailed version was sung in the Royal presence and with Royal approval and I suppose that made it official. But the missing verse vanished from the ken of most of us long before that.

The verse that has been quietly dropped, the one in the middle, ran as follows, and many's the time I howled it in my schoolboy treble:

O Lord, our God arise,
Scatter her enemies,
And make them fall!
Confound their politics,
Frustrate their knavish tricks,
On Thee our hopes we fix,
God save us all!

How this verse got dropped, I do not recall. It just quietly faded away, like old soldiers. I do not remember

continued

seeing it go. Somewhere in the past fifty-odd years, in response to a steadily growing mildness and moderation in the public spirit, this lusty and valiant seven lines fell off the national band wagon. It is perhaps not a curious thing that it should do so but those fifty years of increasing gentleness in the public spirit have nevertheless been characterized by more savage and violent disturbance than any in history.

For those who may lament the bowdlerizing of the Imperial anthem, there is this thought: often when it is played the band or the recording will repeat it three times. The above words are for the second time round.

Death of a Forest Monarch

A report reached a district office of the Ontario Lands and Forests Department that three bull moose were found dead in one small area in the Rice River, and foresters were sent to investigate.

Two of the bulls were dead in the river. The third was found dead on shore, a short distance from the other two.

The foresters found the largest bull standing upright in the mud but dead from drowning, his head under water. Facing him, but simply floating where he had fallen was a younger bull. When the carcasses were winched ashore, it was found that the younger bull had a dislocated shoulder and back of his foreleg was a ragged gash ten inches long. Both bulls had numerous cuts and bruises and one eye of the younger bull had been gouged out.

Through examination of the teeth, the foresters found the old bull was ten years old, the younger one, five.

"The west shore of the creek," writes R.H. Trotter, who investigated, "where the fight had apparently started, was trampled down for an area of about one acre. Several spruces had hair clinging to them where the animals' huge bodies had scraped during the battle which probably lasted for hours on shore, by the look of the trampled ground, before it ended up in the river."

The old bull had obviously driven his badly wounded adversary into the river, where he himself, trapped in the mud and exhausted, had been unable to extricate himself and his huge-antlered head had finally dropped forward into the water.

A little way up the stream, on shore, the third bull, a young one of three years, was found where he had fallen in another furiously torn up acre of ground almost identical with the other arena. This bull was gored and battered by the old monarch as mercilessly as the other.

As those who hunt moose know, a bull moose weighing half a ton can vanish as soundlessly as a fox when disturbed. But in the mating season, he can also be a savage fighter to the death with his own kind.

Table Talk

Sometimes, in a restaurnt, you get seated at a table near a public speaker, lady or gent.

By public speaker, I mean one of those who is not satisfied with the mere audience of his or her table mate or mates, but realizes there is an audience within hearing at adjoining tables. And they cannot resist the impulse to widen their audience.

As their chatter begins to grip your attention, even though you are trying to pay attention to your own table mate, you glance at them, and catch them in the act of glancing at you, to see if they have collected you. Many of these public speakers are pretty good talkers. They know how to tell a story or relate interesting particulars. They start with a catchline, and build to a nice climax.

The thing to do is to pretend that you are surreptitiously listening, eavesdropping, which gratifies them to no end, as you can tell by the way they raise their voices and project them in your direction in appreciation of your having joined the audience. But just about the moment they reach the punch lines of whatever they are relating, you lean forward to your companion, and in a clear, reflective voice say:

"Tell me more about Annie. Is it true she is expecting another child?"

The effect on the public speaker is disasterous. They

muff their punch line. They will even raise their voices, instinctively. They are indomitable. They start all over again. Having lost you once, they don't intend it to happen twice. This time, it is a fascinating piece of news they are imparting. Once again, you let them reach the key sentence of the story, one jump from the climax, so you turn your back, and say to your table mate in an emphatic tone:

"Where's that waiter? This coffee is cold!"

With male public speakers, I have seen them reduced to silence and buttering the last roll in the basket. With public speakers of the fair sex I have seen flushes and petulance so furious their hands tremble.

It's a mean trick. But not as mean as holding public meetings.

Flu Serum—Mark I

Those of us who can clearly recall the deadly flu of the final year of the war in 1918 are now up in years. I missed the full fury of it here at home, when in the autumn of that year, it was filling all our cities and towns with funerals. We got it in our regiment in France during the summer. It was spreading through the allied and enemy armies faster than the wild rumors of it.

But it was a mild form, working up to its full malignity as it passed across the congested trenches full of men,

continued

growing in virulence as it approached Britain, and, in troop ships, crossing in the autumn over to Canada.

Our medical officer was notified that he was to expect a sudden epidemic of fever that might affect the entire regiment. Our's was fortunately out of the line, in rest billets. Being adjutant at the time, I had to get up for the 6 a.m. reveille parade. The company orderly sergeants, some of them looking a little woozy themselves, arrived at the orderly room to report sick parades not of ten or fifteen, but of forty, sixty, eighty. One company, billetted in a barn in the village, did not turn out for reveille at all. They couldn't get out of their blankets in the hay.

The medical officer, by 7 a.m., reported a sick list of over three hundred out of our nine hundred strength at the moment.

His treatment was military. He ordered a rum issue for all the sick, with two quinine pills—army quinine pills.

By noon, the whole regiment was feeling poorly. All parades cancelled, the medical orderlies and stretcher bearers became rum carriers as they visited the billets in barn and stable and farm shed, not with mere water bottles of carefully rationed rum, but with good fat rum jars. By nightfall, it was hard to say who had the flu and who was prostrate with rum and quinine. For there was an element in all infantry units—I can't speak for artillery or engineers—that had a high regard for army rum, and would submit to far worse than quinine for a good shot of it. Some of the more nimble characters were able to shift billets rapidly, keeping ahead of the medical orderlies, who, a little weary from carrying gallon jugs, and doubtless infected with the virus too, were not too particular to identify the pitiful individuals, that, from the depths of their blankets, moaned for a tot.

The next day, the sick parade was over six hundred. But the treatment was reduced. The third day, the epidemic was over. Nobody died. And the whole regiment from that day conceived a new affection for their doughty medical officer.

Hard Times for Mice

It is with great respect I now explode an ancient myth. It is not cheese for mice. It is cheese for minnows and bacon for mice.

Who would have believed that cheese was a good bait for minnows? For years, I have baited my minnow trap with bread crumbs, the traditional bait, or, in desperation, when the minnows did not show any interest in bread crumbs, with broken up pieces of fishworm. But a couple of seasons ago, an old guide who always has all the minnows in the world for sale, told me that if you take a piece of so-called mousetrap cheese about the size of a walnut and drop it in your minnow trap, you can't keep the minnows out.

For years, I have faithfully submitted to the ancient tradition of baiting mousetraps with cheese. Success was moderate, sometimes good. But a farmer much plagued with mice let me in on his secret.

"Bacon," he said. "Either raw or fried. That's the bait for a mousetrap. Just a tiny bit, tied on securely with thread so the mouse has to struggle to get it, so releasing the trap."

Result? All up and down the shore at our summer

continued

resort, I am known as the Pied Piper. Everybody is using bits of bacon rind or left-over crumbs of fried bacon. And the poor little mice that invade summer cottages are succumbing as never before.

In this ever-enlightening age, the number of people who don't even want to trap mice is growing. They spend a lot of time and considerable money in making their cottages mouse-proof and maintaining them so. One of the strangest methods of mouse control practised by the anti-trap faction has been introduced by a professor of the University of Toronto who encourages fox snakes to make their home under and around his cottage. Being a lover of life in all its forms, the professor cannot bring himself to trap mice. But he feels it is morally, ethically and biologically proper of him to invite fox snakes to look after the mouse problem for him in the normal way of nature.

Thus, you will commonly see a good big four or five foot fox snake in the professor's woodbox or reclining in the cool shade under the cottage. It is not unknown for fox snakes to come in the house, following the same secret route of entry the mice do. Fortunately, the big ones can't make it. But I have seen three-footers.

The fox snake is the most royal looking of all Canadian reptiles, and a wonderful athlete when it comes to chasing and encoiling a mouse.

"Does it not distress you," I asked the professor, "to see a fox snake capture a mouse?"

"I look the other way," replied the professor. "I am a soft-hearted man."

What to Do

Into the club car on the Toronto-Montreal train trouped four young fellows of seventeen or eighteen years of age. They were wearing blue jeans and leather windbreakers, "working clothes" as one lady passenger remarked sniffily. They were travelling first class and of course had as much right to the club car as any of us stuffy elders in our business suits.

They were not rowdy, but noisy, with the festive spirit of the elder teenager. In the dignified quiet of the club car, their intrusion created quite a stir. It was not long before they became conscious of the characteristic reproof of their elders, and it did not improve matters. They were obviously not going to be intimidated by a bunch of middle-aged and elderly lofties who wanted to read or converse in dignified manner of what you might call club car or temporary tycoons. So the boys lolled around and chattered in that provocative tone teenagers have, after their voices change for certain.

When they left to go forward into the day coaches ahead to see what better diversion they might find, all we elder passengers got our heads together in clinical groups to condemn the rising generation.

"What has come over the younger generation?" was the theme.

And up and down the club car ranged all the familiar arguments and instances, the lack of respect for elders, the

continued

brashness, the self-assurance, the impudence!

Finally, down near the middle of the car, one old gentleman who had not taken much part in the debate, a ruddy-faced old boy whom, in fact, I had seen smiling rather chummy at the boys when they were present, sat forward in his chair and caught our ears.

"The time has come," he asserted, "when we ought to give fair warning to the young that if they continue to get further out of hand, and refuse to mend their ways, we will abolish them!"

Abolish! The word shocked us.

"Exterminate them," elaborated the old boy with the red face, by not HAVING any more children! That will cure them!"

Of course, most of us in the club car, after reflection, were obliged to realize that that cure was no longer within our means.

Captain of the Hunt–Lost!

Invariably, every fall season there are stories of hunters lost in the bush. Some of the stories each year are going to be pretty tragic. Some are not.

Most of us, actually, have experienced being lost, if we go into the wilds at all. I've been lost several times and the worst experience was also the most absurd. I blush now to tell it.

I was, at the time, captain of the hunt by reason of the fact that our hunting cabin was my summer cottage. It was my job to lay out the day's plans, to see that meals were on time, the guides ready. Being captain is a job you do with considerable pride. Even if you are quite a small man, you swell up a little when you are captain of the hunt.

At the conclusion of one day's hunt, we all met at a certain high rock about three miles from the hunting cabin. It was four o'clock of a dull, sleety day. I directed that my seven companions now return overland to the cabin, with two of the guides leading them safely. I, the captain, would take one guide and go round a big marsh where we might jump a buck. At the far end, the guide would head for his home, in another direction, and I, knowing every foot of the land, would come home to the cabin alone, arriving just at dark.

They left. My guide and I agreed to take opposite sides of the marsh, and at the far end, wave goodbye and go our separate ways. It was about four-thirty when I waved to the guide at the far end of the marsh. I then headed for the cabin, across a country I knew intimately, having hunted it for years.

It was grey and dismal. Sleet was falling. I hustled over rock and gully, through bush and around muskeg, across well-known terrain. And suddenly, coming up over a rock ridge, I faced a large marsh I had never seen before. It certainly had not been there in the morning. A weird, cold panic seized me, which everyone who has hunted will know. A confusion indescribable.

I had about twenty minutes left before dark. I started around the end of the marsh. Every step I took I knew was in the right, south-west direction. Yet every step was in country I had never seen before. Everything was

continued

strange, forbidding.

Just as dark fell, I knew I was licked. I pulled myself together, remembering to be a woodsman, a sportsman. Camp right here for the night. Alas, my friends, with their captain lost!

I found a rock ridge for a windbreak, hastily cut evergreen branches and rigged a hasty shelter, rummaged furiously for firewood, and breathing heavily, was just about to light my fire for the long night watch when I saw a light moving in the trees not seventy-five yards away.

"Hello," I shouted, hardly believing. Had one of the guides already come searching for me.

I ran towards the light. It was Buck Martin, the least woodsmanlike of our party, carrying a lantern.

"Where are you going?" I cried lamely.

"To the privy," replied Buck casually.

I had camped for the night within fifty yards of my own outdoor privy, and seventy-five yards from my own cabin.

On Wave Lengths From Way Back

A good twenty years ago, I lived in a house with one bathroom to serve a large family. And it was the custom for each of us to keep our towels in our own rooms, carrying them to and from the bathroom. To this day, I find myself now and then carrying my towel out of the bathroom.

Unconscious memory is an interesting thing. Two houses and fifteen years ago, the hall light button was on the right hand side as you entered the front door. Hardly a week passes that I do not automatically reach and fumble for a button that is not there.

It is forty-five years since the first great war. Several wars have come and gone since then, and the puttee, that long strip of wool we soldiers of olden times wound spirally up our legs, has been abandoned lang, lang syne. But not a month goes by that, on a wet and miserable morning, when I grumble out of bed, I do not bend over, when I hitch on my trousers, fold over the cuff in two deft motions unforgotten in my deep unconscious memory, hold the fold snug, and glance about for my puttees for one shocked instant while I recollect where and who I am.

Messed

On the radio a gentleman from the BBC was introducing some recordings of band music by the famed regi-

continued

mental bands of Britain. And he came to the place in his announcement where he had to refer to massed brass bands.

What he came out with was "messed brawss bends."

I felt terribly sorry for him, because the minute he said it, he knew he had not done it justice. You could tell by the way his voice quivered. Massed brass bands is a phrase to stump any of us. Imagine how a Scot would say it. Figure out how a Lancashire man would handle all those a's. An Australian would get the massed very much as we Canadians do, but the brass would be different. A Texan would say "mayuss brayuss bayands." A Bostonian of Irish descent wouldn't pronounce it at all, because it referred to British bands, and an educated Bostonian would bring the brass out as brarse.

There is no canon on the pronunciation of English, for the English themselves, who claim to have invented the language, have forty ways of pronouncing it.

And when we hear some poor fella talking about "messed brawss bends," let us figure he is just being local, and do our best not to feel lofty.

I have known Canadians to pronounce Chicago with the Ch hard, as in chicken. But on the air I heard a Chicago announcer giving it the Ch as in chicken. In Chicago they should know better. Have they no sense of history, no civic pride? The word Chicago comes from the Ojibway word shekak, for skunk, shekak-onse being the "place of skunks." The nearest the pioneers could get to shekak-onse being Chicago.

Tronna, Hamil'n, Muntry-awl, Nagra Falls, Edmm'n, we have some pretty place names, too. But their origins are growing a little cobwebbed in the contemporary mouth.

Nature's Radar

The eyes of a hawk are in the sides of his head and look in opposite directions. It cannot therefore focus two eyes, as we do, to sharpen its gaze on distance or upon objects near to it. Yet the vision of hawk related birds of prey is said to be many times more powerful than human vision. Biologists are at work trying to establish some means of measuring the power of vultures' eyes. But until they find some sort of yardstick, we have to content ourselves with marvelling at what these birds of prey can do with one eye.

It is not by smell but by sight that vultures spot the dying or dead animals upon which they feed. An animal no bigger than a rabbit dies. And almost at once, a vulture that was invisible far up or down in the sky, comes floating swiftly and unerringly down to its feast. Some of the Indians of the south and southwest had the notion that there was some mysterious message that was transmitted by death to vultures. A hundred or a thousand years from now, we may discover that there actually is some spiritual or perhaps radar impulse liberated or exerted by death, and that vultures have the power or the instrument for receiving that impulse. Meanwhile, that one eye to the side of a vulture's head, or those two eyes operating

continued

separately in completely opposite directions, scan infinite space in all its complexity of prairie, forest or desert, and, from miles away, detect a rabbit, a fawn, a calf, a tiny mite in vast space. And the great bird comes as swiftly as he can. He must be swift, for a dozen of his relatives have already spotted the dying or dead morsel, and are heading for it too. The mystery of the appearance of vultures from nowhere the instant death strikes or impends has gripped the imagination of cattlemen in the southwest for several generations, and some of them are inclined not to talk about it.

"It's one of those spooky things," a Texas cow hand told me, "that a man don't care to bother about when he's riding around alone so much."

If not spooky, it is at least startling to see one of our own hawks, a hundred feet in the air, turn and dive for a mouse no larger than your thumb which it has detected in the tangle of field or bush below.

Gourmets in the Morning

What do goormies—I use Old Mr. Flood's spelling of the word gourmet—what do goormies eat for breakfast?

What do they have for lunch and supper on week days?

At home, what do their wives cook up for them?

There are gourmet clubs that meet regularly and ritualistically in order to feast upon delicacies prepared by dedicated chefs. There are gourmet restaurants where the devotees of gastronomy foregather to dine and wine with an almost religious fervor.

An interesting question is: what do they eat the rest of the time? With this in mind, I spent a few mornings calling upon my gourmet friends at unearthly hours. The first was at breakfast and eating corn flakes and milk. A half empty can of orange juice sat on the sink, and on the gas stove an egg was frying in bacon grease. When he served himself, the egg had a leather bottom.

Another took me to breakfast at the lunch counter of the corner drug store. Still another was caught in the act of carrying breakfast up to his wife in bed. The toast was burnt on one side, and curled. The coffee was out of a bottle. The marmalade was a well-known supermarket brand.

But you should hear them on goormie parade!

The Sounds of Spring

There is more to spring than the sight of it, the smell of it and the feel of it. There is the sound of it. And city dwellers have no idea what they are missing. For the sound of it, save for the increased tumult of children and

continued

a little more whizz to the sound of passing cars, an occasional robin on the housetop and a rare crow exclaiming overhead at what misery he sees below him, is denied the city and town dweller.

In the country, winter's silence is its chief characteristic. Snow and cold are seen and felt. But it is the stillness of winter that impresses the country people most. So when spring comes with a hundred, no, a thousand sounds, it may be that the sounds of spring are, to countrymen, the most exciting and rejoicing of the season's blessings. The sounds of the cattle, pigs and fowl released from custody: the ringing of birds far and near, but especially far, so that the whole air, in depth, is filled with pattern: the bold notes of wild geese plowing over, and crows rowdying above the distant woodlot; but above everything else, the music of frogs and toads. We city slickers, driving the country roads, hear the sudden din, quickly fading as we get out of earshot, of these spring peepers and the swamp tree frogs. The first utters a single shrill note in rapid succession, and a roadside ditch with hundreds of them all minutely hooting, fills the countryside, for those who live in it, with a faint cloud of sound. The swamp tree frog's note is a staccato trill, very like the sound you make drawing your thumb over the teeth of a comb. They and the peepers often orchestrate together, and every ditch and puddle and pond in field and wood is fairly trembling with their tiny din. We only hear it in passing. But to the country dweller, it is part of the festival of spring, the mood music over which shape the patterns of the birds, the sharp infrequent fife of the groundhog, the far barking of dogs, the exclamations of farm animals, the drummery of woodpeckers, the remote beat of the partridges, and the sound of the wind with something to play with better than empty branches.

But we in the city and town are confined to the jazz of traffic, and the loon cry of jumbo jets.

The Miracle

The real marvel of the age is the small number of people killed and maimed in automobile traffic, when you consider the number of proven fatheads among us who are free to coil and twist in city traffic and to race and lunge at breakneck speeds commonly up to seventy and eighty miles an hour on our highways.

In this stampede of traffic every day are the several hundred of us who have this very day been fired by our employers for stupidity or for disregard of the rules. Among us also are those of us who have got into jams at home, those who have today wrecked their bank account, lost a friend, been caught stealing or missed a chance to make a thousand dollars. Among us are those who hit their thumb with a hammer, broke a dish, fell down stairs, set fire to their bed clothes, cut themselves shaving, ate cucumbers when they knew they would suffer, got five wrong numbers in twenty-four hours. Among us are hundreds with hangovers, hundreds who should have stayed in bed with a fever, hundreds who should have had their eyes tested for new glasses ten years ago.

There is hardly a man or woman or child among us who has not, this day, committed some act of folly which either we regret or have not the intelligence to regret.

But we see nothing remarkable in being entrusted with two hundred wild horses to drive, heel and toe, in the hot procession of our swarming fellow fatheads. It's a miracle.

Fitness

Certain individuals and organizations have been getting away with some pretty derogatory remarks recently about the unfitness and general deterioration of Canadians. Federal aid is being granted to the study of the question and the discovery of means of improving our muscles.

It would be interesting to examine the grounds on which is based the estimates of our deterioration—when it started, what caused it. It was in the first world war that Canadians became aware of the fact that, physically, they were as good as, if not a little better than most other nationals. They proved it when, on their four infantry divisions being organized as a corps to fight as a distinct formation, they became one of the recognized shock units of all the armies, feared by the enemy and held in admiration by their allies.

Yet to raise this Canadian force, the army used no such standards of physical fitness as were employed in enlisting the second world war forces. From city and town, country and bush, the run of the mill Canadians came to the colors and went to live for four years in a squalor, filth, hardship and want of decent food that can hardly be conceived today. There is much more to manhood than muscles.

Onions

People generally either love onions or hate them. There is nothing half-way about onions as there is about pumpkins, turnips, and even apples.

Certain people claim that they are poisoned by onions. As an onion lover, I suspect these are the people who eat a little bit of onion, and then, when their astonished and delighted insides clamor for more, suppose themselves to have been upset by the onion. The truth of the matter may well be that their stomach, on receiving the beautiful taste, and finding no more despatched, put on a sulking match, raised a rumpus, created a scene. It was not yelling for less. It wanted more.

The way to eat onions is wholesale. You should eat onions the way you eat the first strawberries. Who would think of eating half a strawberry? Or corn on the cob? Who would take a bite out of a cob of corn and let it go at that?

There are onions now available, beautiful tender snow white globes, that you can eat like an apple. Some onion lovers would not go that far. They prefer a little onion in their salads, or a whisper of onion in a sauce. Boiled onions with cream sauce or baked onions in their own juice with butter come nearer to heaven. But by long odds, the best way to eat onions is just before you go to bed, in a magnificent sandwich of fresh baked bread, thick sliced onion sprinkled with salt, pepper, a dribble of basil vinegar or a smear of mayonnaise.

Such a light collation, at bedtime, may give you the wildest dreams. You may wake up in the morning wondering what hit you. You may die in your sleep.

But it is still the finest way of all to eat onions.

Pools of Imagination

By the year's end, despite the dismal prospect of three months of snow and slush, the real devotee of fly fishing is already deep into the sport. The gifts he got at Christmas—a fly box, a new fly line, a landing net started him on the way. He had to put the new acquisitions in among his old gear in closet or store room. What more natural than that he should take his old familiar fly rod out and see how it was wintering? What else could he do but note that it needed a touch of varnish and some fresh whippings at the ferrules?

The wives and families of trout fishermen are all too well acquainted with what follows. Fly books and fly boxes have to be re-organized, all the flies taken out and put back according to some mystic order of precedence. Fly lines have to be cleaned, polished and hung on wooden pegs in large loose coils. New leaders have to be tied up, in readiness. It is about now that the true zealot begins setting his fly books on his bed side table so that he can scan their contents devoutly both before going to bed and on first rising.

Lord Grey of Fallodon, author of *Fly Fishing* wrote: "I lay awake in bed fishing in imagination the pools I was not going to see before March. I made a rule therefore, that I would not fish pools in imagination before January the first."

But trout fishing comes earlier in England: and besides, Lord Grey was a strong, silent man.